THE WORLD ALOFT

"If we lived in the ocean of water we would drown. If we lived in the ocean of mud and earth and stone we would be buried. But instead we are in the third and highest ocean—the greatest of the three: the ocean of air.

"The sky begins at our feet. We breathe it. We are actually crawling on the sea bottom of the heavens. We are the crabs of the airy depths."

THE AVIATOR'S BOOKSHELF
THE CLASSICS OF FLYING

The books that aviators, test pilots, and astronauts feel tell the most about the skills that launched mankind on the adventure of flight. These books bridge man's amazing progress, from the Wright brothers to the first moonwalk.

THE WRIGHT BROTHERS by Fred C. Kelly
(23962-7 * $2.95)
Their inventive genius was enhanced by their ability to learn how to fly their machines.

THE FLYING NORTH by Jean Potter (23946-5 * $2.95)
The Alaskan bush pilots flew in impossible weather, frequently landing on sandbars or improvised landing strips, flying the early planes in a largely uninhabited and unexplored land.

THE SKY BEYOND by Sir Gordon Taylor (23949-X * $2.95)
Transcontinental flight required new machines piloted by skilled navigators who could pinpoint tiny islands in the vast Pacific—before there were radio beacons and directional flying aids.

THE WORLD ALOFT by Guy Murchie (23947-3 * $2.95)
The book recognized as *The Sea Round Us* for the vaster domain—the Air. Mr. Murchie, a flyer, draws from history, mythology, and many sciences. The sky is an ocean, filled with currents and wildlife of its own. A tribute to, and a celebration of, the flyers' environment.

CARRYING THE FIRE by Michael Collins (23948-1 * $3.50)
"The best written book yet by any of the astronauts."—*Time Magazine*. Collins, the Gemini 10 and Apollo 11 astronaut, gives us a picture of the joys of flight and the close-in details of the first manned moon landing.

THE LONELY SKY by William Bridgeman and
Jacqueline Hazard (23950-3 * $3.50)
The test pilot who flew the fastest and the highest. The excitement of going where no one has ever flown before by a pilot whose careful study and preparation was matched by his courage.

Read all of the books in THE AVIATOR'S BOOKSHELF, available wherever Bantam Books are sold, or order directly from Bantam by including $1.25 per order for postage and handling and sending a check or money order to Bantam Books, Inc., Dept. WW3, 414 East Golf Road, Des Plaines, IL 60016. Allow four to six weeks for delivery. This offer expires 3/84.

THE WORLD ALOFT

GUY MURCHIE

with illustrations by the author

BANTAM BOOKS
Toronto • New York • London • Sydney

THE WORLD ALOFT
*A Bantam Book / published by arrangement with
Houghton Mifflin Company*

PRINTING HISTORY
*This book is an abridged edition, but with new
material added, of* Song of the Sky *by Guy Murchie.
Bantam edition / November 1983*

ABOUT THE COVER ARTIST

Graduating in 1970 from Farmingdale College, BOB
LARKIN has sought out the widest experience, from
creating horticultural and medical illustrations to doing illustrations for toy companies and motion picture
companies. The artist has built over 150 accurate rep-
licas of model planes made not with the plastic kits
but built up spar by spar. He lives with his family in
East Northport, Long Island.

---

*Bantam Books are published by Bantam Books, Inc. Its
trademark, consisting of the words "Bantam Books"
and the portrayal of a rooster, is Registered in U.S.
Patent and Trademark Office and in other countries.
Marca Registrada. Bantam Books, Inc., 666 Fifth Ave-
nue, New York, New York 10103.*

To the Memory of Our Son
J E D

Contents

Acknowledgments

IN EXPLORING a subject as big as the sky I have come upon so much stimulating material that I have been able to use only a small part of it in this book. And yet for even that portion I am indebted to the generosity and diligence of scores of persons during the ten years it has taken me to get it down to earth and ink.

Most difficult to put into words is my wife Kathe's share—she who labored long to remove distractions and who understood that a man may be working even when gazing dreamily at the sky.

Next I must express my profound debt to Wolfgang Langewiesche, and particularly for his published work which has been so close in subject to my own and of such excellence that it has taken much restraint for me to quote him as few as half a dozen times herein. But far beyond the quotations Mr. Langewiesche has generously allowed me to take from his book, *A Flier's World,* I owe much to him in inspiration and factual information on the subjects of air masses, aerodynamics, the engineering problems of long-range flight, and the mysteries of the sonic barrier.

For much further help and constructive criticism on chapters and illustrations dealing with their special fields of study I am indebted to Professor Charles Franklin Brooks of the Harvard Meteorological Observatory on Blue Hill, to Giles Greville Healey of the Institute of Navigation, to Alfred Holland of the Aeroelastic and Structures Laboratory at M.I.T., and for helpful extra information to Edwin H. Bryan Jr. of Bishop Museum in Honolulu (on South Sea navigation), to Dr. Joachim Kuettner of the Air Force Cambridge Research Center (on the mountain wave, especially material for the text and illustration on pages 120 and 121), to Frederick

Billings Lee, administrator of the Civil Aeronautics Administration (on a number of elusive flying facts), to Captain Daniel L. Boone and Navigator Willie Leveen of American Airlines for the account of their modern saga in navigation.

Inevitably I have also had to delve extensively into hundreds of published sources, among which I feel my largest debt to the following books: the *Compendium of Meteorology* published by the American Meteorological Society, *Cloud and Weather Atlas* by Hugh Duncan Grant, *The Raft Book* by Harold Gatty, *Light and Colour in the Open Air* by M. Minnaert, *Tornadoes of the United States* by Snowden D. Flora, *Great Adventures and Explorations* edited by Vilhjalmur Stefansson, *Admiral of the Ocean Sea* by Samuel Eliot Morison, *Science for the Citizen* by Launcelot Hogben, *Soul of Lodestone* by Alfred Still, *The Wright Brothers* by Fred C. Kelly, *Ballooning* by C. H. Gibbs-Smith, *Wildwood Wisdom* by Ellsworth Jaeger, *Aerodynamics of a Compressible Fluid* by Hans Wolfgang Liepmann and Allen E. Puckett, *One, Two, Three . . . Infinity* by George Gamow, and many others.

Although all facts and anecdotes in this book have been made as accurate as my limited experience and repeated checking by friendly authorities would allow, I myself must of course assume responsibility for all the boners that may still be lurking in the rhetoric. The only intentionally fictitious names used are of flight crew members in a few of the accounts of air accidents where implication of blame might otherwise (perhaps unjustly) be embarrassing to the men involved.

Last and longest I want to express my heartfelt thanks to my friends the publishers who have been so generous and patient with me these many years: to Dorothy de Santillana and Paul Brooks who first had faith in my efforts and gave me sound advice, to Anne Barrett, Austin Olney, and the many others who so skillfully edited and handled the manuscript and illustrations.

G. M.

West Swanzey, New Hampshire
1960

Introduction

THIS EDITION of *Song of the Sky*, especially prepared for the teen-age reader, contains the essence of the complete book as published in 1954 with almost all its illustrations. Although it is only about half as long as the original, it has been updated with corrections of errors and new material added wherever possible.

Inevitably some technical details of navigation, meteorology and aerodynamics are absent, as are a chapter on bird flight and a roster of winds, but the general quality and content of the book is intact. Even the style of writing and fullness of vocabulary have not been toned down, for the author and publishers believe that readers mature enough to be seriously interested in exploring the ancient mysteries and modern problems of the sky are also mature enough to understand them in befitting language.

The Airplane Finds Its Way

1

The Craft

SHE WAS BUILT like a whale, for cargo and comfort. Ninety-four feet long and full-bellied, with wide tail flukes that could ease her nose up or down at the merest nudge of her controls.

Her sinews and nerves were four and a half miles of steel cable and insulated copper wire. Her brain was a set of instruments tended by radio waves, inertia, magnetic force, and atmospheric pressure, and all pivoted on sapphires and crystals of rare hardness.

She was Number 896, one of the original C–54s, the famous flying freighters designed especially for ocean transport —perhaps the most widely used long-range weight-carrying airplane to appear in the decades since man taught metal to fly.

On this night of the fifth of February she floated confidently on a mantle of black air 11,000 feet deep and bottomed by the angry North Atlantic ocean. Her wings were of duralumin, styled to cut the sky at two hundred and forty miles an hour. She rolled slightly—ever so slightly, like a por-

3

poise sighing in sleep—just enough to tick the octant bubble from Mizar by the pole.

Inside her lighted hulk the air was at twenty inches of mercury, or only two thirds the density of sea level. The temperature was 75° Fahrenheit where her crew sat in the cockpit, 52° in the fuel compartment amidships, and 8° below zero outside. Her four motors, representing the heft of 5400 horses, breathed the thin cold air with the aid of super-chargers forcing the vital oxygen into their pipes at a mani-fold pressure of thirty-one inches. Her gross weight at this moment was 62,180 pounds—6200 pounds of it cargo, prior-ity 1A, battened by rope and steel rods to the cabin floor: penicillin from Chas. Pfizer & Co., New York City, destined for London, England, and oxygen cylinders, type F–2, from Firestone Steel Products, Akron, Ohio, marked for Burton-wood, England. She had taken off from Stephenville, New-foundland, amid snow flurries in the late afternoon. She was bound for Prestwick, Scotland, 2296 miles away by the great circle.

We men of the crew sat at our stations, going through our motions, writing words and figures into flight logs, occasion-ally dreaming, or talking, or unbuttoning a little with ca-price. From the flight deck we could not see the waves two miles below. There were dense clouds covering the sea and the sun was deep under the earth. In the western sky Orion and the gibbous moon swung downward at fifteen degrees per hour. And as the earth turned and the planets turned, the galaxy of the Milky Way moved on its inscrutable course through the black universe of which man knows not the be-ginning nor the end.

"What are you doing up here? Why is that octant in your hand?"

It could have been the wind asking. I was the navigator seated at my chart table in the airplane's cockpit, gazing into the darkness beyond the window. The wind—a wind which never existed before the airplane—was crying in long mono-syllables like a Chinese bird-monger. "Why—wh-h-y—wh-wh-h-h-h-y-y?" It sprang full born from the Plexiglas nose and exploded upon the duralumin skin, sprawling backward over the humps of the astrodome and the engines, tearing itself cruelly on each protruding edge of cowling, each pitot and spar. It was the invisible substance of which the sky is made—not just air, not just wind, but a stuff which is part of the insoluble consciousness of flight.

"Why is that octant in your hand?"

Because I am the navigator.

I hold the needle that will pierce the cloud. I sing the song of the sky.

While flying the ocean I am plainly the busiest of our crew of five. I keep account of the airplane's position and track over the earth, of altitude and the passing cloud layers, of horsepower and consumption of fuel. My flight log sometimes contains scores of entries in a single hour. I work with wind, radio waves, sun and stars, with charts of many colors, with tables heavy in figures.

Frequently I converse with the pilot who likes to know where we are, how long before we will get to such and such a place ahead on the map, or how much gas is left in our tanks. Pilot on this flight is Captain Blake Cloud who sits up front in the driver's seat, a wiry little man with pale brown eyes that blink nervously from behind his oxygen mask. He is the ranking officer of this Douglas-built C–54, this ocean-wise dragon of the air.

Second in our hierarchy is Gullerman Dropford, the co-pilot or first officer who sits on Cloud's right with a duplicate set of controls. He graduated from Yale and appears to veer to the conservative.

I am third in command, followed in rank by sleek Ernie Silvers, flight radio officer, an ovate Lothario whose desk is opposite mine in the cockpit, and Ignatz Wuzienski, flight engineer, a gangling Texas lad who sleeps most of the time between his few routine check duties while in the air.

We are all serving as employees of American Airlines in this first regular transoceanic round-the-clock freight service that the world has ever seen. We sense our place in history as pioneers of a great age of air transport that will defy time and space and weather and future dangers of extreme speed and altitude of which we have hardly yet begun to learn.

I put the octant back into its case and glanced at my airspeed indicator. The needle pointed to 166 knots. My thermometer read 6° below. The altitude was 11,000. Magic needles quivering before me—needles of light in the darkness. Adjusting my slide-rule computer in a familiar calculation, I read off our corrected or true airspeed: 184 knots. That was the actual speed at which the sky's air was passing us.

Jotting down the airspeed in my flight log, I glanced next at the fuel-flow meters on the main panel to see the rate of gas consumption. Again by some familiar figuring I found the true hourly rate and recorded it in the log.

Then for exact altitude I had to correct the altimeter needle reading for barometric pressure and temperature, working it out on my computer: 10,850 feet.

While checking my compass against the pilot's compass, I noticed that Cloud and Dropford had fallen asleep. It is not unusual to find both pilots dozing in the vast stretches of the sky's ocean, and I have sometimes known this state of affairs to continue for more than an hour while the automatic pilot faithfully guides the plane, continuously correcting the controls according to the dictates of the compass and the altimeter—the needle guiding man through the sky even while man's mind is not there to see it. It is a minor miracle that this can happen. And it is also customary for the radio officer, whose instruments are of least use in mid-ocean, to sleep part time in the air, to say nothing of the engineer.

I suppose there have been times when the entire crew of a plane slept over the ocean for fairly long periods without ill effects, but the navigator is one who definitely should not sleep for it is his serious responsibility to keep constant track of progress. He must note any change of speed, direction, or any factor of temperature, altitude, or engine adjustment that might affect the speed. If he does not, he loses a clue to accurate reckoning—which would be like a detective overlooking a bloodstain at the scene of a murder.

You earth lubbers who have not yet flown the ocean might suppose an aerial navigator is often worried about getting lost. This is not the truth. The navigator is accustomed to threading his way through the sky. His is a long view on time and space—and his mind knows the fullness of its freedom, bounded only by navigation's prodigious outer margins of safety: the multiplicity of precision instruments, four engines, three radios, the fuel reserve, hand pumps that can duplicate hydraulic pumps, the emergency equipment, the self-reliance of five men.

2

The Way

FROM WHERE I SIT here in the sky, the world of waves and ships and men below seems far and somehow small. Yet human history has it that this life up here sprang from that down there—that eons of blind earthbound toil and erring struggle had to pass before man hatched out the simple secrets of the birds.

Have you heard how the ancient Arabs found their way for hundreds of miles across desert and sea? How the American Indians moved unerringly through the uncharted wilderness? How the island dwellers in the South Seas sailed confidently over the entire Pacific?

These things are the thin brave seeds that we are now harvesting across the sky, the first heritage of aerial navigation.

How did he do it, the Arab?

We will put ourselves in his sandy footprints. We are on the desert—alone but for a flock of scraggly sheep and goats moving across yonder gravelly slope. Our duty: to watch the flock. Otherwise there is little to occupy thoughts as the sun goddess swings slowly overhead each day, leading her myriad star children on their nightly caravan.

We hardly need to wonder that the familiar star Alphecca passes always directly overhead, for here near El Ala it has always been so. The wise old men and the Jews all tell of it. In fact when we are many days' journey south on the desert,

8

faithful Alphecca always shows us the way to El Ala just as surely as the famous star of Bethlehem is said to have led the wise men to the birth bed of the Christian prophet. Similarly Alpheratz points straight down on Mount Sinai, Albireo on Tebuk, Hamal on Medina, and Markab on the great southland of Sheba. Each star is a beacon showing the way to its own part of creation.

We Arabs, like most others in this early time, do not think of places in relation to a globular earth, but rather to the paths of the sun, the stars, and the wind. Our world is the fullness and breadth of Arabia with seas and mountains and cooler countries far northward and, some say, hotter countries far southward under the sun, with all around vast oceans and rivers from which no man has yet lived to return. If any of us ever saw a map it had no lines of latitude or longitude, but it may have included star paths or perhaps arrows showing the big winds: the simoom, the belat, the asifat, the zaubaat.

For on land, as at sea, in the ancient days it was the winds that told direction almost as much as the sun and the stars. The winds usually did not swing with the hours and could therefore be used as reasonably steady indications of direction, as indeed could the ripples the wind left in the sand.

The stars gave the Arabs only latitude—northness or southness—because latitude was the only thing in the motion of most stars that was constant. One star alone seemed to stand always in the same direction: a certain low star in the north. The sun was fairly trustworthy if one studied her wanderings with the seasons, but the moon was capable of almost anything and it required a man of oracular power and rare patience to fathom his inveterate waywardness.

As Arab navigation science grew spasmodically with the centuries one of its greatest strides came when Arab seamen first built dhows big enough to leave the coasts and brave the Sea of Oman to the Indian Ocean. It was then that they plotted the rising and setting points of fifteen stars, picked for distribution at almost equal intervals around the horizon so that, added to the true north and south, these formed the thirty-two points of the compass known today as N, N by E,

NNE, NE by N, NE, NE by E, ENE, E by N, E, E by
S . . .

The Arab compass points of course had Arab names and
were associated with specific winds so that ships could be
steered at angles relative to the wind when the stars or the
sun were out of sight. The northeast trade wind was one of
the most reliable of these. Like the other winds, it could be
recognized by its individual and seasonal qualities of dryness
or dampness, by its temperature, swiftness, and tempera-
ment, thus giving the Arab helmsman an easily verifiable
wind bearing.

Another early navigation device much used by ancient
seafarers was the shore-sighting bird. This was a preview of
our dimension, for the bird's vision in flight gave man one of
his first means of obtaining bearings at sea in stormy
weather, a time when bearings are most welcome. Indeed
ravens, cormorants, doves, and many other species of land
birds in cages were customarily taken along on ocean voyages. When in doubt about the direction of the nearest
coast, the navigator could release a bird and watch it circle
for altitude. If it eventually flew in a definite direction the
assumption could be reasonably made that it had seen land
that way. If it did not find land, a bird which could not rest
on the sea would have no choice but to return to the ship.

The earliest of known navigators, Noah, is reported in the
Book of Genesis to have used exactly this system in guiding
the ark. Having had the benefit of a weather forecast from
God Himself, to say nothing of fine specimens of all the
birds on earth, Noah was well equipped by the standards of
the day and watched with unruffled calm as "the fountains
of the great deep were broken up, and the windows of
heaven were opened."

His huge craft, said to have been built of gopher wood
(probably cypress), took off and rode the face of the deluge
for "fifteen cubits upward," even over the mountains. For
forty days and forty nights the downpour continued without
let—a record. On the forty-first day the sky at last looked so
much cheerier that the great navigator confidently opened
his hatch and "sent forth a raven" which flew searching "to
and fro." No land in sight.

Next Noah tried a dove. "But the dove found no rest for the sole of her foot, and she returned unto him into the ark . . ." Seven days later again Navigator Noah "sent forth the dove . . . And the dove came in to him in the evening: and, lo, in her mouth was an olive leaf, pluckt off: so Noah knew that the waters were abated from off the earth." He also saw the direction (NNE) from which the dove returned.

After still another wait of the customary seven days, Noah dispatched the dove for the third time "which returned not again unto him any more." But he had noted the course (E by S) of its flight to shore and, reassured by his double bearing, safely brought the big ark in and made a perfect landing.

Peoples in forested countries of course had a different problem in navigation. Since it was easier to find food, shelter, and fuel in the woods, most of them neither kept herds like the Arabs nor often traveled great distances. Judging latitude by the stars does not appear to have been a widespread accomplishment of the American Indian, though he certainly learned to take bearings by the North Star and probably could tell time by the circling Dipper.

Rather did the Indian navigate the wilderness by little clues of direction found in trees and plants, by deer or buffalo trails, by observing waterways and mountains, sometimes by a signal thread of distant smoke. He was taught in childhood to notice that the tips of evergreen trees inclined slightly to eastward, bowed by the prevailing west wind; that moss and bark are slightly thicker on the moist north and northeast side of trees, and tree rings consequently wider there; that the gum oozing from the spruce is clear amber on the south side but dull gray on the north; that compass goldenrod tips bend gently northward, and the leaves of prickly lettuce, rosin weed, and prairie dock all lean more north or south than east or west.

Stalking proved to him that the north side of a hill is the quiet side—because the ground stays damper there and thereby deadens sounds, while the dry south slope is often treacherous with rustling leaves and hidden crackly sticks. The loon and the duck, he observed, prefer to breed on the western shores of lakes and rivers. The flying squirrel and the pileated woodpecker dig their holes on the east side of trees. But the spider spins her web on the south side, the favorite resting place of the sun-loving moth and the fly.

Though probably the world's best tracker, the Indian nevertheless often blazed his trail as a navigation aid, bending saplings, stripping bark, planting forked sticks in streams, or piling cairns of rock on cliff paths above the timber. On the prairie he used simple grass signs to indicate direction, such as knotting the grass into bunches and pointing the top right or left to show the way. For long-range broadcasting when smoke signals were too temporary, he used the famous "lop stick" sign, many examples of which are preserved to this day in ancient virgin trees of former Indian country. This signal was made by precise lopping off of branches of these prominent trees on ridges where their coded pattern messages could be read for many miles.

It would be only natural for the South Sea Islanders, who grew up close to the thundering surf and ate and slept with its sound and smell in their ears and noses, to be masters of ocean navigation. Obviously if their ancestors had not already successfully sailed the sea they would not have been there in the first place.

So one need not be surprised to learn that these "Vikings of the sunrise" regarded a third of the earth's surface as their private lake across which they could go in any direction and at any time. But it may be news to many that the first of their tools of navigation was the wave. To the islander the wave was like a tool, for it was studied and measured to a degree not to be exceeded anywhere until the latter days of oceanography. In fact, as we use radio and radar today so did the South Sea navigator a thousand years ago use the ocean wave. He did not merely steer by the angle of the wave, but he observed the whole pattern it made around an island, and the swells and eddies—affecting the very shape of the atolls and the coral reefs and the channels through them.

He recognized the differences between the ripple, the wave, and the swell—how the tiny ripple changes with each puff of breeze as it laces the greeny slope of the wave, how the wave keeps on rolling despite a momentary lull or sideways gust until the wind as a whole shifts to another quarter, and how the great swell may persist in one direction all day or night against wind and even waves which have swung around the compass to oppose it, sometimes outrunning the wind altogether to give warning of the unseen typhoon like a dog before his master.

The South Sea people who advanced this particular study to its greatest perfection were the Marshall Islanders, who inhabit one of the more northeasterly groups of atolls fought over in World War II. These black-haired Micronesian navigators made elaborate charts out of ribs of coconut palms tied with fiber to form a meaningful framework indicating winds, swell systems, and the eddying junction lines where swells meet. Shells on these rib charts represented islands, and sticks were placed to show how far offshore the coconut palms could be seen, or how far out one could detect the indentations on swells made by the ebb of a lagoon tide.

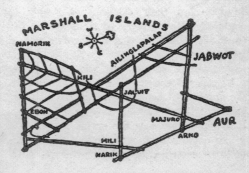

Most of the charts represented the conditions around single islands or small groups, each being a kind of cryptic notation made by an individual navigator to aid his memory and to instruct his heirs in a particular oceanographic situation. But some charts have been found which represented large sections of the Pacific and showed on a grand scale the interlacing patterns between one island group and another—lines of swell eddies in some places stretching in series for a hundred miles, forming cross-wind bearings on each island, each peninsula, each reef.

The full significance of all these subtle manifestations of wind and wave is almost impossible for modern man to appreciate until he flies over an island archipelago in one of the calmer seas, knowing in advance just what to look for. The great primary swells are almost always quite visible as seen thus from the air, their lines revealed in moving shades of green and blue according to the changing angle between surface and the light. So too may the eddy beams be seen, and if you look sharp you can usually pick out the fainter echo swells in gentle weather. Tuning in on them all from a sailing canoe on the surface a thousand years ago was of course navigational sleuthing of the highest order.

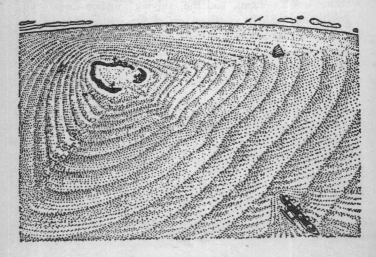

The South Sea Islanders naturally used much more than wind or waves for compass and bearings. In mid-ocean the sky was for them a compass, clock, and map, all in one—and it had the advantage of being permanently built in, at least most of the time.

Time by the sky clock was highly developed in the South Seas, for the navigators had long recorded the stars' custom of rising earlier each night (by about four minutes in our modern way of measuring), and of course the regular nightly and seasonal rotation of the Southern Cross. The Tahitian day was divided into six watches (each of two hours by a modern clock), and the night the same.

Distance was a vaguer dimension to these men, for it was geared to human effort, not merely to the earth or the heavens. The Polynesian had no word for distance, no thought of space apart. Time and direction were his important measurements. Funafuti was not 450 miles away but five days' sail toward the star Rigel. The tops of palms could be seen not from nine miles but from two watches of paddling into the wind.

Shore-sighting birds, however, perhaps another heritage from the Arabs, were used in navigation by the Pacific islanders, as by the Phoenicians and Vikings in the Atlantic. The island navigators kept the frigate (man o' war) bird for this purpose, for this forked-tailed sea bird does not normally land on water but heads for the nearest land. It is still a common pet on Ocean and Nauru Islands in the central Pacific.

And careful records of bird migration from island to island, of bird nesting places and feeding and roosting habits, undoubtedly gave many a handy bearing in the lonely reaches of the great deep. If boobies and gannets are seen flying in the late afternoon the navigator can safely follow them toward land for they are commuting home from their fishing grounds to feed the family. In the remote Galapagos area of the Pacific, cormorants and pelicans indicate shore, being rarely found as much as twenty-five miles from land. And if at night or day he hears the cries of sea birds of any sort the South Sea Islander can be sure land is near, for these must be gulls and no true gull but the northern kittiwake strays far from his low-tide hunting grounds along the coast. The sea birds that follow ocean vessels many days out from land are usually terns, fulmars, petrels, shearwaters, skuas, jaegers, or one of the great southern family of albatrosses—all of which keep peaceful tongues at sea.

When seafaring Polynesians in Tahiti sought new land for their privacy further southwest in the ocean, what could have been more natural than to observe the repeated yearly migrations of land birds in that direction, and follow them? Did not the long-tailed cuckoo fly always southwest from their islands? Knowing that the cuckoo cannot rest at sea, the Tahitians could follow it with confidence in their great double canoes, spaced wide apart in a long file for visibility. And, like the cuckoo, they actually landed in New Zealand 2500 miles away.

Even butterflies can give vital bearings to ocean navigators, and the monarch butterfly has been known to fly nonstop for thousands of miles across whole oceans. They fly low and are easily seen, but since their flights are sometimes suicidal in result, the direction they came from is a better indication of land than the way they are headed.

Undersea creatures and fish likewise give important clues, since the numerous coastal species rarely venture out with the few oceanic kinds like the blue shark, bonito, sunfish, and flying fish, the air-breathing porpoise and whale.

Land-smelling mammals have at times served the function of shore-sighting birds, and it is known that the Tahitians carried pigs for this purpose, because the sensitive snout of the sea-weary pig would sometimes show excitement at approaching land long before it was visible even to a flying bird.

As the clouds serve as beacons, hovering over unseen atolls beyond the horizon, reflecting the pale green of the lagoon or the white of sand, as dawn thunder may hint of a mountainous coast, so does the color and temperature of the sea also yield its clue to the navigator's ocean store. Blue water is salty, warm, and deep, and speaks of the tropics where evaporation is great and dilution small—the Sulu Sea, the Indian Ocean, the Gulf Stream. Green water is cool, pale with particles, thin with river and rain, often shallow. In the tropics it means land, just as in the north with white jigsaw ice it means a frozen bay is close.

Of course most of the great early feats of navigation have been lost to human memory by now, and in the unwritten millenniums great discoveries had to be made many times to overcome intervening ages of forgetfulness until finally they came to be recorded.

Among the primary inventions of man, the sundial was almost as important in navigation as it was in astronomy. Making a calendar and navigating a ship depend, in fact, on the same kind of knowledge and are hard to keep apart, which is something to be remembered if you would clear up the mystery of the fourth dimension.

As man learned to herd as well as hunt, to mine as well as forge, to sow as well as reap, the seasons became more important to him and he studied how to measure them, how to keep records. His first true writings: the score and tally. His first god: the sun.

Stonehenge in Britain and the sixteen Inca towers in Cuzco were elaborate early models of the sundial. Being large of dimension they could measure accurately the sightings of the sunrise at the solstices and the equinoxes, the polar point, the zeniths, the months, the days, the hours.

The medicine men, the priests—astrologers, navigators, alchemists—these wise men of science of their day did their best to bring order and sense into the discordant life of earth. In Babylon they measured and decreed a neat year of 360 days, which seemed too wonderful to be wrong. To match it, they apportioned their circle into 360 parts—ancestors of the 360 degrees we still use.

The Mayans did a closer job of measuring. They made a god of the planet we call Venus and adopted a Venus year. They clocked the planet's circling of the sun to the second decimal: 583.92 earth days of time. To even out the earth days in a Venus calendar year the Mayans dropped four days at the end of every sixty-one Venus years, and an additional eight days after every three hundred Venus years. This unique calendar used for many centuries by a people who had no telescope was so accurate that had the Mayans continued it to the present, the accumulated error over this period of more than a thousand years would have amounted to only a day.

The Eskimos, who had a rare sense of place and made good maps, easily measured the midnight sun and the noonday dawn and forecast the exact dates of the solstices. So did the Hawaiians, who called the northern limit of the sun at Cancer "the black, shining road of Kane" and the southern tropic at Capricorn "the black, shining road of Kanaloa." The equator they named "the road to the navel of Wakea," the center of the world.

And other peoples in Egypt and Crete, in Babylon and Greece, in Norway and Persia and far China were also exploring the world, trying out ideas and inventions—all of them together constituting a new attitude, a quickening of the plodding pace of history that was expressed most dramatically of all by Friar Roger Bacon in thirteenth-century England when he shouted to complacent mankind: "Experiment, experiment! Cease to be ruled by dogmas and authorities; look at the world! . . . Machines for navigating are possible without rowers. . . . Likewise cars may be made so that without a draft animal they may be moved . . . And flying machines are possible, so that a man may sit in the middle turning some device by which artificial wings may beat the air . . ."

If this spirit did not immediately rouse all the thinkers of the earth it was at least an overture to the astonishing doings of the Portuguese two centuries later. There had been a good deal of hit-or-miss discovery in the world throughout the millenniums, but Prince Henry the Navigator of Portugal organized discovery on a month-to-month basis and got consistent results that led directly to the first Mediterranean-to-India sea route as well as to Columbus' eye-opening demonstration that the earth was bigger and more potential than anybody had ever dared believe.

It may seem surprising that Columbus, who was an educated man by the standards of his day, should not have known more of the accumulated navigational science of the world, especially since he had navigated widely—including "in 1477 in the month of February a voyage a hundred leagues beyond the island of Thule called Frislanda or Iceland" where he had noted the long winter nights caused by "the narrowing of the sphere." The fact is that by no means all the world's navigational knowledge had been collected even by Prince Henry's endowed institution, and Columbus was a devout Catholic—a man with a mission, guided more by spirit than mind—a redhead who had learned the ropes the hard way and would not trade his "arte de marear" for all the fancy tabulations and astrolabes and brass scrimshaw in Christendom.

The things that were known in 1492 to some men but not to Columbus, the things he might have known but evidently didn't, make an impressive list:

That the earth is nearly 25,000 miles around, approximately as Eratosthenes announced in 250 B.C.

That the earth circles about the sun, as Aristarchus of Samos explained in 270 B.C. and would soon be demonstrated anew by Copernicus in his *De Revolutionibus*.

That it is possible to sail around Africa to the Indian Ocean, as Necho's fleet proved in 600 B.C. and da Gama was about to rediscover.

That it had long been possible to navigate with precision across four thousand miles of ocean, as the Polynesians had done for many centuries in the Pacific and the Norsemen had almost equaled in the Atlantic.

That a great unmapped land lay west of Iceland and Greenland, as discovered by Leif Ericson, Karlsefni, Snorri, Bjarni, Thorhall, Hoei Sin the monk, of course the Indians, and probably the Polynesians.

That the truer polar point in the northern sky was then 3° 27′ from the star Polaris, as the best of the astronomers knew, and that failure to correct for the discrepancy might cause an error in figuring latitude of two hundred miles.

That latitude may be found also by observing the sun's altitude at noon, as long used by Moslems in their "camel navigation" on the desert.

That longitude may be found by observing the moon's exact declination (distance from the celestial equator), as theorized and developed in Alexandria at the time of Ptolemy and referred to by the monk Gerard of Cremona in the twelfth century.

That a ship speed at sea may be measured by a waterwheel and tally pot into which a pea is dropped at each revolution, as perfected by the Romans more than a thousand years earlier.

That direction and nearness to land can often be detected by careful observation of swells and eddies in the sea, as practiced by the Polynesians for untold centuries.

That land can be spotted by releasing a land bird at sea, as known to navigators at least as early as Noah.

The truth seems to be that Columbus was not particularly well equipped for his great ocean voyage of discovery, not even as well provided in respect to navigation as Prince Henry's ships coasting down West Africa way forty years earlier with their astronomers, their bronze peloruses, astrolabes and lunar tables. He had neither sufficient knowledge

nor means at hand to get any aid from the stars except a
simple visual indication of north from the north star, which
his compass could do as well, and a vague judgment of latitude by guessing the altitude of the pole. His printed material consisted of an ordinary traverse table, a multiplication
table, a Bible, an *Imago Mundi* and a copy of *Ephemerides*
of Johannes Müller intended for astrologers.

How then did the Admiral of the Ocean Sea, appointed
by their imperial majesties of Castile, get across the Atlantic?
How did he navigate?

It was by simple dead reckoning, some good breaks,
plenty of old-fashioned courage and skill, and co-operation
from the Almighty.

They used to call it deduced reckoning, shortened it to
ded. reckoning, then punned it: dead reckoning. We now
usually call it just D.R. It was a good ninety-eight per cent
of the navigator's art in 1492, especially in the narrower "climates" of the north where stormy weather often hid the sun
and stars for days at a time. It is simply the process of keeping track of how fast you are going, in what direction, and
when you change to other speeds or directions. It means
plotting your hourly and daily positions on your chart as you
go, and being able to deduce the net result of your various
trackings into a definite position for any moment of time.

As a former map maker Columbus of course knew how to
plot positions and draw his own charts of new lands. If he
had had better ways of telling direction and speed, and better maps, he could have gotten more accurate results. If he
had known how to check his dead reckoning with the stars
or with known land positions, he could have been more
accurate still.

The fact that Columbus had almost no knowledge or faith
in celestial navigation does not make him a bad navigator.
Few sea captains knew any more about the stars than he in
1492 and he largely made up for his celestial deficiency by
extraordinary attention to D.R. and by liberal use of the lead
line in strange waters.

Columbus always carried several lead lines for sounding,
and frequently used them. Besides the standard forty-fathom
lines on each vessel he had a few deep-sea lines of a hun-

dred fathoms. On at least one occasion he was known to bend two of these together to make a 200-fathom sounding. This was probably in the mysterious Sargasso Sea which appeared to presage land or shallow water. If the Admiral was worried about running on a reef while plowing through the weed nothing could be more reassuring than the splash of the plunging 200 fathom line and oft-repeated cry, "No bottom, sir."

Yet even Columbus grew negligent about sounding when he got used to the steep shores of Cuba, and on Christmas Eve in 1492 his flagship ran aground and was hopelessly stove in before the next tide.

How did he keep track of speed? Did he have some primitive kind of speedometer? No, his system was nothing more advanced than spitting over the side and watching the spit float by, or tossing in a chip, or simply watching a fleck of foam go the length of the vessel—judging its speed by guess and by gosh, perhaps counting out the time or pacing the deck abreast a wave. A good sailor can judge speed that way within about ten per cent—perhaps half a knot on a sailing vessel.

A century or so later a more accurate system was devised of heaving a small log of wood overboard attached to a long line with knots tied in it every fifty feet. The log was allowed to drift aft for half a minute, timed by a special log glass; meanwhile someone counted the number of knots paid over the rail—which equaled the number of nautical miles per hour (knots) the ship was making. But Columbus never heard of knots. He just made a good guess and translated it into Roman miles per hour. That was that, and no arguing with the captain.

What about time? How did Columbus keep track of his tacks or changes of course in the sea? The medieval ship's clock was the half-hour sand glass, known to Columbus as the *ampolleta*—and which remained in general use in the British Navy as late as 1839. The gromet or ship's boy in each watch had the duty of minding the ampolleta, reversing it promptly when the sand ran out. Eight ampolletas or glasses (later: eight bells) made up the four-hour watch that is still standard on ships all over the world.

Of course the ampolleta was not a precision clock for, even though it may have averaged within fifteen seconds correct per half hour in its test run in the glass factory in Venice, a heavy sea could slow it up a couple of minutes each turn, or a sleepy gromet much more between turns.

It is well known that Columbus kept two charts: an accurate but secret one for himself and a false-front chart to keep his worried shipmates from thinking they were so very far from home. This double play was quite understandable under the circumstances but the Admiral might just as well have saved himself the trouble. Ironically his "phony" chart was nearer the truth than his nine per cent overestimated "accurate" reckoning. That was the way of God and of dead reckoning in the fifteenth century.

For almost three hundred years more the question of how to find longitude at sea was to continue to be navigation's main unsolved problem, just as it had been that of Columbus —and it was not until Captain James Cook sailed to the Antarctic Circle late in the eighteenth century, becoming the first man in history to reach a zone of the earth never before seen by human eye, that longitude reckoning attained its first important practical success. The reflecting sextant meanwhile had made it possible to take accurate celestial readings at sea by eliminating the swaying plumb line, thus giving latitude by the pole star or the noon sun. But longitude (over which the sun and stars sweep about a mile every four seconds) was another matter, which explains why the British government by the Act of 1714 offered a reward of £20,000 "for any method to enable a ship to get its longitude with an error not exceeding thirty miles at the end of a voyage to the West Indies."

This offer not only provoked tantalizing dreams among the inventors but a flurry among the clockmakers, some of whom had heard that finding longitude at sea was no harder than finding a peacock's egg on the thirty-first of June. Weights and water gave way to pendulums and springs, springs became hair springs, balance wheels and cycloidal suspension were added, and centrifuge governors led to verge escapement which turned to anchor escapement. And still the clock would not keep good time at sea—especially, be it noted, during changes of temperature. Whereupon came a Yorkshire carpenter named Harrison, who instinctively knew it was the peahen who lays the eggs, and he made expansion-compensated pendulums and compensated balance wheels—and behold, his fourth model chronometer in a test voyage to Jamaica in 1761 produced a longitude error of only one mile.

While Harrison was still trying to get His Majesty's exchequer to come across with the £20,000, fellow northcountryman Cook sailed south and west (with a Harrison chronometer aboard, set to Greenwich), and eastward around the antarctic barrier—and he always knew the time in Greenwich, therefore the difference between Greenwich time and his own local sun time, therefore his longitude—in hours and minutes, in degrees of arc. And that is part of why Australia is British today: because King George's lieutenants were first to know their longitude.

Arctic navigation presented some different problems: the compass was unusable near the magnetic pole and during the equinoctial twilight neither sun nor stars could be seen for months of the year. However Shackleton almost reached the south pole in 1908 and Peary, traveling Eskimo-style in the cold season to avoid the dangerous thaws, attained the north pole in April 1909. Within three years the south pole too was reached independently by Amundsen and Scott—and the bigger exploratory navigation jobs of the planet Earth were at last complete.

This did not mean that all of the world was yet known or understood, nor that the science of navigation had much more than started. Navigation devices have often had to wait for earlier inventions or discoveries to clear the way, just as in the other sciences, in the arts, in life itself. While the printing press led to reading, and reading to eyestrain, eyestrain created a demand for spectacles, spectacles led through optics to the invention of the telescope, and the telescope revealed the planets as being round, revolving, earthlike bodies

with nights and days and moons and motion about the sun.
Thus the printing press not only gave the navigator printed
handbooks and almanacs but spectacles to read them with,
and new observations from the heavens with which to devise
better navigation and write better books. Its by-product tech-
niques of cutting type went hand in hand with better methods of cutting balance wheels for watches, thus accelerating
still other interdependent technologies and steadily creating
a whole new philosophy of progress—an idea neither the
Greeks nor the Chinese had ever known but which was so
soon to revolutionize the West through the pooling of knowledge, the concept of postulation, the humble magic of trial
and error.

So on the earth below I see the trail of struggling men
and ideas leading upward in our wake. I remember the patient ploddings behind us: the oxcarts, the rickshaws, the
steam engines, the horseless carriages, the balloons, the gliders. And their music is in my ears.

It will be part of us always. It is our past—the airplane's
past—in a way of thinking, the past of all air and wind and
sky.

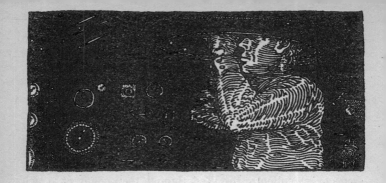

3

The Needle

I TURNED my table lamp low so that I could see the stars better. The window glass was clear as air. Moving my head to different positions I feasted my eyes on the cosmopolis of sparks that lit up the entire vault of space.

It was a friendly cosmopolis and familiar by now, like the lights of greater New York as seen by a pilot from Jackson Heights. And I had a warm feeling for those little sparkling stars.

But it was high time I got a celestial fix. We might be half an hour behind flight plan by now and accurate navigation was getting more important with every minute.

I moved my stool under the astrodome and climbed upon it. It was my angel footstool, my stepway to the stars. I never have quite gotten used to this function, this measuring of stars.

When you glance casually at the moon or see a star twinkling at you through a treetop it seems farfetched to think that those remote celestial objects could be put to any practical earthly advantage such as earning your living or bringing you closer to a full and happy life.

Yet here I find myself harnessing the moon and stars to these very ends. And my mind is opened to the fullness of many continents through star-guided travel and other magic that enables me to thread my way across the sky.

But how does navigation work? Of what is the needle that guides the thread?

Navigating is not higher mathematics. Contrary to a general impression, you do not have to be a chess champion to understand it—even though a liking for chess might suggest a certain aptitude. What you need most is the kind of mind a good secretary has, or an efficient switchboard operator, or a natural-born paperhanger. You have to be accurate.

The simplest form of aerial navigation is pilotage: point-to-point flying by following a succession of landmarks on the ground. It is the easy introduction to the needle. It is simplest in fair weather and daylight, more difficult at night, and impossible over the open sea or clouds.

When you first fly over the earth, map in hand, you may feel like a fish out of water. The earth does not look much like the map unless you happen to be over some dramatic feature like a lake or coastline. You may be so confused by the checkerboard of fields and woods and farms down there that you don't notice the more permanent details that really count. Map makers seldom put woods and fields on their maps because these things are only the window dressing of the earth, the fleeting smile on the face of the world: too often these touches of make-up change overnight as the loggers' chain saws, the bulldozers, and the farm tractors do their work. Instead you must train your eye to catch the patterns of more permanent things: river beds and canyons and hills and lakes and railroad lines and the towns and larger highways, which are, relatively speaking, part of the flesh of the earth. These also of course may be altered by dams and great new projects of man, but usually slowly enough for the map makers to keep up with them.

Good pilotage is an art and to be learned only by flying and looking and seeing, by cultivating a sure eye for permanent pattern and indestructible detail, and a sense of north and south, a thoroughness in checking canals and stadiums, quarries, airports, and reservoirs. That it can be treacherous is well known to any experienced pilot and there are innumerable examples of this.

One that comes to mind is the predicament of a veteran navigator I know who was flying up a Greenland fiord in a C—47 in 1942. It was broad daylight and there seemed to be almost no problem in navigation. He knew he was in the right fiord and it was simply a matter of following it up to the landing field—or so he thought.

With the mountains all around dazzling white in the sunlight between moving cloud shadows, the navigator felt at ease as he listened to the hum of the two big engines. Now and then he gazed down upon the deep blue of the salt water with here and there a chunk of greeny-white iceberg floating. It was a fascinating scene and it did things to the mind. While one mountain seemed to be trying to lunge out at the plane, another appeared to crouch as if to spring into the clouds. And then the moving plane stood still while the mountains drifted by like arctic demigods breathing and sighing in the sun.

He couldn't say when he first noticed it but he found himself conscious of a great mass of mountain wall ahead of him. Behind it, somewhere around a bend in the fiord, was the sloping field of Bluie West One set on a gravelly bar underneath a glacier. He did not look at the mountain wall very closely. It was just another white mass flecked with cloud shadows and it was several miles away. For the moment he was basking in the glow of a massive ridge ribbed with snow soaring over his right wing tip. The ridge was bedecked with hanging gardens of ice that appeared to float through space from one precipice to the next.

Then as the navigator noticed that some of the snow on the mountain was moving faster than the rest of the mountain, suddenly WHISSSSSH! The plane shuddered and the mountains were gone. The sky was gone. The sea and the icebergs were gone. Everything outside the window was white—blinding, dazzling white.

The navigator was confused. He gasped. The co-pilot had been flying but the pilot now looked up from the pile of A.T.C. forms he had been filling out and quickly grabbed the wheel.

"I'll take her," he said, dipping his left wing and turning sharply.

The navigator now realized they had run into a cloud in the fiord, a white cloud unseen against the white snow.

The pilot intensely watched the compass and the artificial horizon, made a 180° instrument turn in the fiord, straightened out and—Whissssssh!—the curtain was away and there were the mountains and the sea again.

It is not pleasant to have to make that kind of maneuver blind in such a narrow spot. The strain is severe on the needle in the cloud. But such a slip in observation is one of the ever lurking hazards of pilotage and sometimes even experience and care are hardly enough to avoid it.

However it is when the ground becomes continuously invisible in fog or gloaming, or the course leads over the sea, or the map shows no detail, that pilotage must definitely give place to instrument navigation, to the elemental mathematics of dead reckoning aided, if God is willing, by the radio or the stars.

The basic form of navigation beyond simple pilotage is, as we have said, dead reckoning. It uses almost all the navigator's current tools of trade: the compass, pelorus (for measuring visual bearings), computer, octant, altimeter, thermometer, airspeed indicator, driftmeter, fuel-flow meter, radio and so forth. As in Columbus' day, dead reckoning is still the backbone of navigation, and it is still done by pricking off points on a chart with dividers.

Dead reckoning in the sky is similar in main principles to the ancient sailor's art but different in emphasis, in detail. We in the air have to think of such things as our sideways drift before the wind, even as did Columbus. That is part of keeping track of our direction. And of course we must measure our speed.

However, we must work faster in the air because we are moving so much faster. For every minute we take in figuring out our position, our position moves several miles ahead.

And the factor of altitude is something new that was added when we took to the sky, the third dimension.

Instead of the old lead line for sounding the sea bottom, for instance, we have altimeters to sound the sky bottom as we float above it. The basic purpose is much the same.

Altimeters are of two kinds: the pressure altimeter, which is really a barometer and works on the principle that air pressure decreases with altitude, and the radio altimeter, which is a radar instrument and measures the actual distance to the ground below by timing the echoes of radio waves. Both of these are modern counterparts of the old lead line.

The pressure altimeter tells you your height above sea level if you set it for the sea level pressure of that time and place. The radio altimeter tells you your height above sea level if you are over the sea or add correctly the height of the land below you.

Thus each altimeter has its limitations and it is the combination of the two that gives the best results. In flight we get reports of sea-level pressure as often as practicable by radio so we can set the pressure altimeter correctly, and we read a map to keep track of the height of the ground below us so that we can use the radio altimeter effectively.

In some ways, however, flying is still more like Columbus' voyages than like modern sea navigation, for flying is riding the wind, and sailing ships are much more affected by the wind than modern streamers which need hardly notice anything short of a gale. As a sailing vessel skids a little sideways in the sea so even more does an airplane drift sideways in the air. There are modern ways of measuring the sea slip of a surface ship, and even better ways of measuring the side drift of an airplane.

Did you ever meet that basic instrument of aerial navigation, the driftmeter? It is something like a submarine's periscope but, being in an airplane and above the surface instead of below it, it points downward instead of upward. As you press your eye into the rubber eyepiece and gaze down the shaft through the floor of the airplane toward the earth you see objects or clouds or waves of the sea moving steadily rearward under you. You also see a set of luminous grid lines which are built into the instrument to help you measure the drift. As you watch the trees or the whitecaps on the waves steadily moving back, you twirl a knob which turns the whole driftmeter shaft including the grid lines until you line them up parallel to the motion of the things you see. Once that is done you can read off your drift in degrees to right or left on a scale attached to the instrument.

A normal drift for a large modern airplane is something between zero and ten degrees, but the faster the airplane the less the drift because the weaker the wind will be in proportion to the speed of the craft itself. A supersonic plane or a rocket, for instance, will seldom have a drift of more than a couple of degrees.

When you catch the concept of drift you already have caught the idea of the wind triangle, which is fundamental to dead reckoning in the sky. The three sides of this triangle represent: (1) the heading of the airplane or the direction and distance that would be flown during a unit of time if there were no wind, (2) the actual track of the airplane or the direction and distance it flies during that time with the help or hindrance of the wind, (3) the wind itself or the direction and distance the air moves in that same length of time.

As you can see in the illustration below, the difference between where the airplane would be without wind and where it actually is with wind is exactly what the wind did during the time under consideration. Thus if you know exactly what the airplane is doing you can tell the wind, or

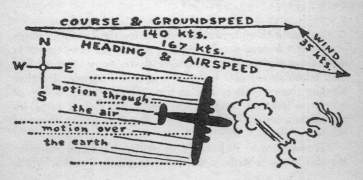

if you know the wind you can tell what the airplane is doing.

This is the basis for predicting drift ahead of time (by wind forecast) and thus figuring out what heading to fly: what point of the compass to aim the nose of the airplane at. Naturally the airplane will seldom travel in exactly the same direction it is heading, but you still have to know which way to head it.

Groundspeed is a word you use a lot in the air because it is a basic concept and something you are almost constantly seeking or checking. Groundspeed is your speed over the earth (land or sea) as distinct from your airspeed or speed through the air. Airspeed can be read off the airspeed indicator, but groundspeed usually has to be calculated from clues. Without it you can't possibly know how long it will take you to get to where you are going. With it you can figure your E.T.A. (estimated time of arrival). The E.T.A. is one of the end-products of navigation. It has to be checked and re-checked as you continue your flight, for on its accuracy depends the safety of the flight, the security of fuel reserve, the whole plan and basis on which you are flying. If you are optimistic as to your E.T.A., you are optimistic as to how many miles you are getting from each gallon of gas. And that in flying is optimism that doesn't live long.

Navigation is a pursuit of truth. Since the keeping of records is an obvious boon to verity, navigators are trained in meticulous log keeping, in writing down every scrap of factual information they have at frequent intervals. By thus keeping track of where he has been, the navigator is sure of where he is going. And by knowing when he got to places behind him he can tell when he will get to places ahead of him.

His records are not entirely in written log form, however. He also keeps records in the form of graphic charts, which give him a whole vivid picture at a glance. This is particularly important in regard to the very vital matter of fuel supply in relation to distance flown and distance to be flown. So the navigator always keeps a graph showing miles flown on the horizontal co-ordinate and gallons of gas consumed on the vertical, with a slanting black line or curve indicating the planned fuel consumption (each point on the line being as far to the right in miles as is correct for its height in gallons). In addition to this line of planned fuel consumption plotted before the start of the flight, the navigator draws a red line showing his actual fuel consumption as he flies. And there are other lines on the graph showing what to expect in fuel consumption if the plane should have to turn back, if one of the engines should quit, if two engines should quit . . . And a point is plotted beyond which there wouldn't be enough fuel to turn back: the point of no return.

This graph is universally known as the Howgozit, for its one big purpose is to answer the eternal navigation question: "How goes it?" Are we doing all right?

An interesting case is the terrible forced landing of the *Bermuda Sky Queen* in the North Atlantic on October 14, 1947. The giant flying boat had taken off from Foynes, Eire, the afternoon before bound for Gander, Newfoundland, with a crew of seven and the largest number of passengers ever yet booked for a transatlantic flight: sixty-two, including twenty women and twelve children.

This was not a regular airline flight and evidently no Howgozit graph was kept. When the big plane had winged its way half across the ocean the crew reported they were "well satisfied with the progress of the flight and expected no difficulty." But not long after that the navigator suddenly discovered the head wind was stronger than he had thought and the plane was not as far along as it should be. Just then the engineer inexplicably "missed a couple of hundred gallons he thought he had." The crew checked as best they could and figured out they had already passed their point of no return and still had not enough gas to reach land ahead. They had gone bankrupt without realizing it. They would have to ditch the plane at sea.

Luckily there was a weather ship still within range, Ocean

Station Charlie where the U.S. Coast Guard cutter *George M. Bibb* was watchfully riding the gale about one hundred miles west of mid-Atlantic. The *Sky Queen*'s young pilot, Charles Martin, headed for it, homing in on its radio, and with great skill landed in the dangerous cross-seas close to the *Bibb*.

It took more than twenty-four hours of heroic effort before the rescue was completed, almost miraculously amid torn life rafts and stove-in surfboats crashing up and down in the thirty-foot waves, women and children and men being fished out of the icy sea and hauled painfully aboard the heaving cutter by long ropes looped under their armpits. The plane itself was a total loss.

Besides knowing his point of no return before every ocean flight the navigator must figure out alternate places where he can land in case his destination socks in with fog or closes for some other reason. This happens not too rarely in the moody North Atlantic region and even when blind-landing systems are operating, an airport may be closed on account of high wind, heavy snow, flood, fire, or accident.

Almost anything can happen in navigating the ocean. Not long ago a plane was flying a load of passengers from Casablanca to New York. After stopping at the Azores it took off for Newfoundland, but less than two hours later a report came that all landing fields on Newfoundland were closing on account of fog.

As the point of no return was still a long way ahead, the crew turned the plane around and headed back for the Azores. But before they got there they were stunned to hear by radio that fog had folded up every Azores airport also.

Hastily scanning his maps in all directions the navigator now discovered that his only possibly alternate was in Africa. So back they flew and had just enough gas to land once more in Casablanca to the exasperation of the passengers who had confidently expected by this time to be coming into New York.

One of Confucius' most famous sayings is that "a man who has made a mistake and doesn't correct it is making another mistake." That comes close to being the ideal slogan for a navigator. Everybody makes mistakes; but a navigator must be a fellow who keeps mistakes and their consequences at a minimum by checking them continually, not only allowing for errors but correcting them as fast as they are discovered. It is specifically to safeguard against the danger of errors that he writes out a flight plan before take-off and checks it on the ground with his pilot and the flight operations office. That is standard practice and it has saved a lot of lives.

The captain and the operations officer must decide whether the flight is worth making on the basis of the figures given. While the captain naturally holds out for his fuel reserve, the operations man holds out for his payload, and they try to cram as much of both as they can into the maximum weight permitted. It is a squeeze and a compromise, and is mixed up with all sorts of other factors and problems. Some old, some new ones—all challenging.

Did you ever wonder why planes even today do not more often fly non-stop from New York to London, or from Istanbul to Madrid? It is strictly a matter of business. They don't land at way stations like the Azores and Newfoundland just to take a breather or to let on passengers. The crew gets a rest there, it is true, while another crew takes over—but the real reason is to save fuel, to reduce weight for other things.

It is easy enough for a plane to fly all the way from New York to Rome without stopping once, and it is faster and safer than having to land at various intermediate points. But how many passengers is there room for? How much freight?

Saving fuel is important in the air because fuel is expensive. This is almost as true of kerosene for jets as of the highest octane gasoline. It isn't the manufacturing cost; it's the transportation. Since it is being carried by air express its cost is a lot higher than you'd think: somewhere around $10 a gallon. So pause and consider. If you want to play it a little safer by taking a hundred extra gallons, that will cost you $1000 more. It would be much cheaper to take out some more insurance, say a mere $100 worth, and swallow your apprehension. If it were your airline what would you do?

Once in the air of course such questions become only academic. Then the navigator replaces plan with performance. He uses his experience, his aids in navigation, to get there as intended.

It is interesting to consider just what his navigation aids are, their order of importance or relative value. This is one of the fundamental sequences of nature. By general consensus of opinion the basic order of navigation aids is: (1) human brain and body—for thinking, seeing, and doing, (2) map—for knowing what's on the earth beyond your sight, (3) pencil—for marking your course, for checking, recording, calculating, (4) compass—for finding direction, (5) watch—for keeping time. These aids are in the right order for Columbus as well as for the most up-to-date modern navigation of sea or air. Of course one could add flying instruments: (6) airspeed indicator, (7) altimeter; and then a long list of more minor aids: radio, sextant, almanac and tables, driftmeter, directional gyro, computer, protractor, straight edge, dividers . . .

That's the way we navigators think of it. But many a man who flies without navigation doesn't know of these relative values until he learns the hard way.

I remember one pilot who took off in an SNJ one afternoon on a quick "easy" flight from Norfolk, Virginia, to Washington, D.C. He left so fast that he didn't even think of checking his radio. His passenger had an urgent appointment.

As they took off into the setting sun he discovered he couldn't contact the tower. But that didn't worry him. He thought the frequency must be a little off, and he would fiddle with it in the air at leisure.

For navigation he drew a straight course on his map, estimated a correction for the wind, and worked out a compass heading. He planned to tune in on a Washington range station as soon as he had the radio going right, and then come in on the beam.

But as he worked at the radio, he soon realized that it was

seriously out of order. He couldn't get anything but a gentle whine: no recognizable signals at all.

It was now dark and there were lights down below. Towns drifted by. What towns? Was that Dunbrooke or Dunnsville? Or maybe Tappahannock? He didn't know.

He veered to the right. Surely he would find the shore of Chesapeake Bay, or the Potomac, or something. But thick clouds appeared and it was very dark and he couldn't see anything that looked familiar.

When he had flown as far as Washington but saw no sign of any big city he thought of starting a square search, the standard, expanding, squared-off spiral course for most efficient location of a known point when you are lost in its general vicinity. But he had no plotting board and, as he said later, "I didn't see how we could be far off anyway." So he just kept on flying and hoping.

With the throttle and mixture controls set for "maximum endurance" he zigzagged back and forth looking for some clue and was increasingly amazed that none showed up. When his gas got down to five minutes flying time he looked for a place to land. Seeing none, he told his passenger to get ready to bail out. And then the plane sputtered and started to descend. Both men jumped.

The pilot's chute opened nicely but let him down at the same rate as the circling pilotless plane which kept going around and around him, twice missing him by what seemed like a few feet. His passenger landed in a big tree and broke off branches all the way to the ground. Almost miraculously both men were unhurt, and even the empty plane made a passable landing. It was found later undamaged in a field.

Putting it mildly, this adventure is a fine example of how not to navigate an airplane, and yet that pilot probably had been flying his way for years without mishap. Maybe he still is. It would be interesting to know how many other flyers Saint Christopher has pulled strings for, how many have said, "I don't see how we could be far off anyway," and lived to tell it.

We all get our share of breaks, good or bad, but experience shows it not wise to lean on the old boy too hard, trying his patience with our "famous last words." I can see him now in my mind's eye holding starry-eyed figures up above the waves as their mortal lips roll out the familiar death-tickling remarks: "It's over in that direction somewhere."

"Don't worry. I've been flying through them mountains all my life."

"Two hundred feet? Hell, it'll be two thousand easy by the time we get there."

"Only scattered thunderstorms. Let's go."

"All we gotta do is fly half contact and half instruments."

"What did he say the altimeter setting was?"

"Never mind the check list now. We'll have plenty of time in the air."

"We don't need a log this trip. I could navigate this one with my eyes shut."

"My D.R. must be wrong. I just know we couldn't be that far off course."

"Why go back? We can always land at that emergency field if we have to."

"We've got plenty of gas. I'm sure Joe must've filled her up."

Even after the navigator has learned not to utter any of these famous last words, nor to think them, he must somehow get along with his pilot. The lives of all depend on a certain minimum degree of co-operation.

I once flew with a pilot captain who distrusted me, and things were difficult. I found out afterward that he distrusted all navigators. On one occasion he refused to fly the ocean by day even with both sun and moon in shooting position because he believed only the stars were sufficiently reliable for a celestial check. Another time on a westward crossing he mistook Newfoundland for Labrador and we got in safely only because he had a saving grace: he distrusted himself even more than he distrusted me.

A navigator friend of mine solved a somewhat similar

problem by diplomacy. When his pilot refused to make a correction of 30° in heading because "we couldn't be that far off," he got him to change 10°. Twenty minutes later he asked for another 5° and got it. Half an hour later, some more. Thus, little by little in inconspicuous doses he accomplished his purpose and finally brought the plane safely home.

That is the kind of adaptability a good navigator needs to have. He must sometimes outthink his own fellow crew members and, in a modern jet liner, that can mean three pilots, two engineers, a radio operator, a purser-cook, and four stewardesses. His job is less glamorous than the pilot's, but in the crises it is apt to be a key position.

A tragedy that resulted in part from lack of co-operation between navigator and pilot was the case of the Transocean C–54 that wound up in the drink off Ireland in August 1949. I had been a navigator with Transocean Airlines only eight months earlier but didn't happen to know Tim Gruber, the navigator involved.

Transocean is an unscheduled airline that grew up rapidly after World War II. In 1949 it was carrying mostly freight to Europe and returning with DP's and other emigrants it had contracted to fly to South America. On the ill-fated flight the four-engined N–79998 took off from Rome at 4:08 P.M. with a load of forty-seven Italian émigrés who were to settle in Venezuela. There was a crew of eight and a guest pilot: the famous woman flyer, Ruth Nichols. The immediate destination was Shannon Airport near Limerick, Eire.

Until it got dark at about half past seven Gruber kept track of his position largely by pilotage, for he could plainly see the earth: the mountains and coastlines of Corsica, the blue Mediterranean, the great waterfront at Marseilles where Pytheas embarked, and then the Rhone valley and the green patchwork of southern France.

At 8:50 he was over Rennes by dead reckoning but it was dark and undercast and he had no check on his position. In this particular airplane the navigator's desk was not equipped with head phones nor any sort of radio direction-finding device and Gruber had to rely on the others. First Officer Ball, who was acting as pilot while Captain Edward

Lessey rested in the crew's quarters, told the navigator he had not taken a radio bearing on Rennes on account of bad static.

Nearly an hour later Gruber saw lights that looked like the northern coast of Brittany below and thought he recognized where he was. To be absolutely sure, he shot a three-star fix just afterward, which approximately verified the position.

By this time Captain Lessey was back on the flight deck and Ball in his pilot's seat was still trying to get a radio bearing. As the static had quieted down somewhat he presently managed to get a signal from Brest coming from a direction about twenty-five degrees to the left of his tail.

Lessey, perhaps a little sleepy, guessed that the plane must now be just southwest of the Cherbourg peninsula and asked Gruber if that were so: "Aren't those the Channel Islands off to the right there?"

Gruber agreed that that must be correct. And he concluded that the plane must be about on course even if a little behind time. He was sure enough of this not to check further for the time being. He relaxed, perhaps copying a little data into his log or conversing with one of the radio men. He may have passed a few minutes in talking with the celebrated Ruth Nichols who occasionally stepped into the cockpit to see what was going on, or to try her hand at the wheel of a 54.

This, incidentally, was to have been the final leg of Miss Nichols' flight around the world. Years earlier Amelia Earhart died while trying to be the first woman to fly completely around the globe and at this moment Mrs. Richard Morrow-Tait was nearing completion of a somewhat similar feat, but Ruth Nichols was bent on nosing her out in the stretch.

Tim Gruber had calculated his groundspeed from Marseilles to his celestial fix to be 138 knots, a suspiciously low figure under the existing conditions. But a little later when he saw land again off to the right, land which had to be England if the last land had been Normandy, he refigured his groundspeed on that basis and it came out 160 knots, a much more reasonable amount. He felt reassured more than ever now in his identification of those lights which must surely be the towns of Penzance and St. Ives at Land's End.

So he handed a slip of paper to the radio operator and the report was flashed to Shannon Radio that the plane was over Land's End at 10:27 and the E.T.A. was 11:45.

Shortly after this Lessey let down from 8500 feet to 3500 feet which was just over a layer of broken clouds. Gruber stowed his navigation equipment preparatory to landing, and perfunctorily drew on his chart the courses of the Shannon radio range which was being received, the signal being that of an "A" quadrant. He had no feeling of impending disaster. The radio was now practically free of static and the weather was clear except for the cumulus cloud layer below which was becoming more and more scattered. About the only thing Tim Gruber felt a little unsure of was his E.T.A. Thinking it over, 11:45 seemed a bit too soon to make Shannon in view of his earlier slow groundspeed, so he averaged out his groundspeeds and got what appeared a more conservative figure: 12:10. This he gave to Captain Lessey as his final estimated time of arrival.

When 12:10 had come and gone, Gruber did not feel alarmed at first. Perhaps his estimate was a few minutes too early. As was customary he had left the final approach and landing to the pilots. After all, hadn't the main navigating job been done by then? Even if it hadn't, an entire flight from Rome should have been possible for any experienced pilot without a navigator at all. There were several radio range stations along the way, almost as many as in parts of the United States where pilots have always done all their own navigating.

Furthermore, it could be argued, a navigator deserves some respite near the end of a trip for he is the only man in a flight crew whose work becomes harder and more important as the airplane leaves the vicinity of places to land. After take-off, as the crew settles down to a long flight, the pilots can relax or sleep most of the time, the engineer has almost nothing to do except in emergency, and the radio officer usually soon finds himself within effective range of fewer and fewer radio stations—particularly on an ocean flight. But the navigator must keep track constantly, and the further away from a place to land the more vital his work.

It was only natural then that Gruber would relax when the airplane seemed to have reached its destination and was approximately over the airport. And it was natural that he should be surprised at about 12:15 to hear Lessey throttle down the engines but then suddenly turn to him with a demand as to where in hell is Shannon anyhow.

When Gruber admitted he was confused, Lessey asked him to get a quick fix on the loran visual radio. He tried but, as has often been the case in this area, no satisfactory result could be obtained. On the audio radio a faint "N" signal could be heard on the Shannon range, but which one of the "N" quadrants was it and what part of the quadrant? None of the crew could be sure.

Meanwhile Lessey continued flying at a fuel-conserving pace to the northwest, hoping that somehow Shannon would still show up ahead. Gruber, now abandoning both D.R. and radio as a solution to the mystery, hastily unpacked his octant again and shot another three-star fix. By 12:45 he had it plotted and it showed the airplane's position 175 miles northwest of Shannon. On this evidence Gruber suggested turning around and flying a southeasterly course back to Shannon.

Lessey, however, flew almost due south for a few minutes, then southeasterly, aiming to intercept the westerly leg of the Shannon range. This he hit at 01:14, whereupon he turned due eastward to follow the beam straight to Shannon.

By this time all the crew were fully alert to danger and were calculating as carefully as possible exactly how much gasoline was left and how much longer they could stay in the air. Some thought they might just be able to make Shannon, but it was obviously very doubtful. The airplane had been in the air a total of nine hours and six minutes, and only an hour and a half of fuel remained. Captain Lessey sent a distress signal to Air-Sea Rescue facilities at Shannon, giving his estimated position and course.

Some of the origins of the dilemma were by now apparent even to the crew of the doomed plane. They remembered that they had arrived a half hour late at Ciampino Airport before take-off in Rome. To make up for lost time Captain Lesssey had divided preflight duties among the crew. He and Gruber and Second Officer Davis got the weather forecast from the local weather office. Davis then prepared the flight clearance and filed it with Rome Air Traffic Control. First Officer Ball made out the weight and balance manifest. Captain Lessey went to the aircraft, while Gruber computed his flight plan based on a route to Shannon via airways and over both Marseilles and Paris. As the investigation revealed afterward: "the navigator and the first and second officers did not confer, nor did either the navigator or second officer have knowledge of the correct aircraft weight and fuel load until after the flight documents were completed and they had reported to the aircraft. Captain Lessey (who was responsible for all) did not examine any of the documents before take-off."

As an example of what this lack of co-ordination could produce, Second Officer Davis had indicated on the flight clearance that the airplane carried sixteen hours of fuel, but Gruber based his flight plan on twelve hours. Different as these figures were, if either one had been correct the disaster would have been averted. In actuality when these two men got aboard the plane they discovered that only 2260 gallons, or 11⅓ hours, of gasoline were on board.

At a consumption rate of 200 gallons per hour (a standard estimate of the company) 2260 gallons was less than the legal minimum required by Civil Air Regulations. But Lessey had then decided that in view of the predicted good weather some distance could be eliminated by flying straight from Marseilles to Shannon, leaving out Paris, and also by changing the alternate destination from Paris to Dublin, which he did but without reporting it to Rome Air Traffic Control. With these changes there seemed to be enough reserve gasoline, enough at least to satisfy regulations. So it was not necessary to waste time putting any more in.

As the woeful plane flew eastward, her throttles now set to stretch every remaining gallon to its maximum, some of the other errors that combined into calamity also became evident to the crew. There were of course obvious errors in navigation. Not only was Gruber's celestial fix off the French coast wrong by several scores of miles, causing him seriously to underestimate his groundspeed, but he was several degrees off course to the left for some still undetermined reason. He also plotted his bearing on Brest incorrectly and, perhaps partly influenced by Lessey's misjudgment as well as his own errors, mistook Land's End for the Cherbourg peninsula and later thought the southwest tip of Ireland was Land's End.

This double error in recognition of coasts that look somewhat similar at night is understandable, but less excusable was the sequence of errors combined with it, such as Gruber's admitted carelessness in copying down the "A" quadrant of the Shannon range as "N" and the "N" quadrant as "A." This final slip diabolically fitted in with the earlier errors to create a fairly plausible illusion, which escaped detection by anyone on the plane until too late.

The pilots too had their customary share in the navigating, especially in listening to range signals, and they should have kept track of which quadrant of the Shannon range they were in. But evidently they relied entirely on Gruber, while he in turn left the supposedly easy homing in on Shannon largely to them. Thus as each casually assumed the other was doing more than he actually did, there was a considerable gap of error and misconception between them.

And so, her fate sealed from hours past, the big plane with fifty-eight persons aboard finally faltered less than fifteen minutes from her destination. Her engines sputtered and stopped one by one and she glided rapidly downward to the sea just seven miles off Lurga Point, Eire.

The landing was good and the aircraft came to rest in the water without serious injury to anyone. The rubber life rafts were launched satisfactorily, but the panicky Italian émigrés who didn't understand English jumped into the water instead of waiting their turns to climb into the rafts, and seven of them drowned before they could be picked up in the confusion and darkness. Also Jack Haskell, one of the radio men, was hit by a piece of the tail assembly as it broke apart in the waves and he fell from his perch on the fuselage into the black water and drowned.

By the time the airplane sank, fifteen minutes after the

ditching, rescue planes were overhead and flares and additional life rafts had been dropped close to the scene. A couple of hours later the British trawler *Stalberg* arrived and by sunrise had picked up everyone, including all eight bodies of the drowned. Even Ruth Nichols, little daunted by her adventure, soon managed to board another plane and was still able to beat Mrs. Morrow-Tait to be the first aviatrix to fly around the world.

Fortunately it is seldom that a man is permitted the official rating of navigator without some aptitude for the work, but on rare occasions it turns out that a persistent person manages to squeak by all tests on some combination of memorized formulas, bluff, and luck. This of course is all too apt to lead to disaster, as actually happened on May 25, 1952, when a lost British Overseas Airways airliner crashed in French West Africa 1300 miles off course!

Both captain and navigator in this astonishing scheduled flight held second-class navigator's licenses, but the captain had earned his only on the third attempt while the navigator had barely made the grade on his fifth try. Among their unique combination of errors was mistakenly setting the variation control of the gyrosyn compass at 60° West instead of 6° West, which resulted in a heading of 54° off course during much of the six-hour flight. Although several star shots were taken neither captain nor navigator was alert enough to notice that the wrong stars had been used and when the magnetic compass disagreed with the gyrosyn the captain unaccountably pronounced it "unserviceable." Obviously several optimistic assumptions were made and accepted without checking.

Ever since the second-century days of Ptolemy, and no doubt earlier, navigators have been struggling to avoid just such mathematical errors and slipshod thinking. In fact Ptolemy himself was of enormous help to them, both as a teacher and a model of scrupulous care, for his work on the foundations of trigonometry and on star movements was so good that no man surpassed it for 1400 years. Even today his basic calculations in rudimentary celestial navigation stand as the most convenient system ever devised. Although they are a representation only of the *apparent* movements of the sun, moon, planets and "fixed" stars, since Ptolemy assumed the earth was the center of creation and had almost no idea of where or what or how big was the sun, still they make practical sense: they work with a kind of provincial simplicity and even, in the light of relativity theory, are a reasonable aspect of total reality.

With this thought I stand in the astrodome and shoot the stars. This is the highest branch of the navigator's art, the most reliable check he has on his dead reckoning once he is out beyond the sight of pilotage points and the hearing of radio beacons. It is nearly absolute. Although based on the earth view it is otherwise independent of the earth or anyone on earth beyond the airplane. It taps the cosmic relationship between earth and heavens, between the finite and the infinite.

How does it work? How can the navigator pick two or three stars, then take up his octant and in fifteen minutes fix his position within a radius of ten miles? How does knowing his way among the stars enable him to find his way to anywhere on earth?

A three-star fix is really three separate clues which, put together, give the navigator a pretty definite idea of where he is—or, more exactly, where he was when he did the "shooting." That means that a flying navigator is seldom as sure of where he is as of where he was about a hundred miles back. This relative sureness is a kind of function of the speed of modern life itself.

It is occasionally possible in celestial navigating to do most of your calculating ahead of time by a process known as precomputation (computing on the basis of forecast assumptions), thus enabling you to know where you were a shorter distance back. But a disadvantage in this method is that you must first compute how long it is going to take you to compute. And if you should compute longer than you'd computed you'd compute, you must compute all over again.

A three-star fix is similar to taking your bearings in a city park at night from three tall lampposts. If you "shoot" one of the lamps with your octant and discover its light is 60° above the horizontal ground level, you know that you must be somewhere on the circle around the lamp from every point of which the light appears at that same 60° altitude. Thus, even if it is too dark to recognize paths, trees, or other landmarks around you in the park, if you can identify the lamp on a map of the park, you can figure out your distance from it and draw a circle with that distance as radius around the position of the lamp.

If you now shoot another lamp, you can plot yourself a second "circle of equal altitude" around the second lamp. Since you must be somewhere on both circles, your only possible position is at one of the points where the two circles meet, the point that is consistent with your dead reckoning.

The third lamp's circle is not usually essential, but if it also passes through the same point, you can be that much surer of exactly where you are.

So I swing my octant in the direction of Regulus and set

it to the height of the star. I have wound up the instrument's averaging mechanism and now I press lever number three with the little finger of my right hand. The clockwork starts recording the altitude of Regulus' image in my eyepiece, balanced at exactly the same level as the luminescent bubble floating in kerosene in the octant's bubble chamber.

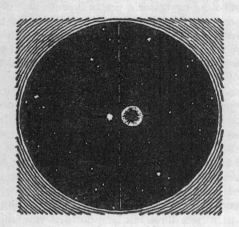

This bubble theoretically remains level, acting as an artificial horizon from which to measure the star's altitude. It would of course be possible to use the real horizon if that were visible, but the aerial navigator so seldom sees any real horizon while flying that the bubble has been found more practical. Besides, it saves having to make correction for one's height above the earth, which would influence the angle between a star and the real horizon.

It is not a hard trick to pick up, this star shooting. Once you have learned your stars you should be able to use the octant satisfactorily in a week. You just stand in the astrodome on your stool, choose a star, set your instrument to what you estimate its altitude to be, aim it, adjust it, and then start shooting: balancing bubble and star together.

When two minutes are up, this type of octant drops a screen across the field of vision, which tells you that the averaging mechanism has stopped. Immediately you observe the exact time by your hack watch and calculate the time of the middle of your period of observation: one minute ago. A "hack watch," by the way, is a common watch (usually worn on wrist) as distinct from a chronometer.

Exactitude of time is of the essence in celestial navigation, because every four seconds' error in time causes about a mile error in fixing your position. So it behooves you to reset your hack watch frequently by your pocket chronometer, which can be checked at least daily by radio time tick. The reason for the averaging mechanism in the octant is of course that the bubble is not as steady as the real horizon. It inevitably lurches about as the airplane yaws and porpoises in the sky, thereby making it necessary to observe a star over a period of time to average out the bubble's caprices.

Once you have recorded the exact heights of the three stars, you have some calculating to do. The principle of this is that you assume a position near where you think you actually are. You pick some spot in latitude and longitude that is handy to figure from and, using your air almanac and celestial tables, calculate what the heights of the three stars would have to be if you had observed them from this assumed place at the exact time you did your shooting.

Then, noting what differences there are between your computed heights and your actual observed heights, you can easily correct your assumed position into a real position, plotting on your map the circle of equal altitude for each star. Of course you don't need to draw the complete circles, which might go around the earth, but only the parts of them near where you are. For practical purposes these short pieces come out as straight lines, and the three of them form a triangle. The smaller the triangle the more accurate the fix and the center of the triangle can be considered your most probable true position.

It is easier to see the resemblance between this and the lamppost fix if you visualize the center of each circle of equal altitude as being exactly under its star. That center is called the substellar point and is the spot on earth nearest the star. It corresponds to the base of the lamppost, in this case a lamppost so high that, practically speaking, it can be considered infinite.

Thus sitting at night in the black sky beneath the stars I see the heavens harnessed according to the mind of Ptolemy, all the stars at the same (infinite) distance from the earth. The sky is a hollow sphere around me, studded with stars. It seems a kind of greater earth turned inside out.

Except for the sun and its satellites, which move along the general line of the ecliptic, all the stars are fixed in relation to the celestial co-ordinates just as islands and cities on earth are fixed on the terrestrial co-ordinates of latitude and longitude. As the earth rotates, the celestial sphere of Ptolemy with axis through the North Star appears to revolve toward the west around the earth—with the earth seemingly motionless at the hub of creation.

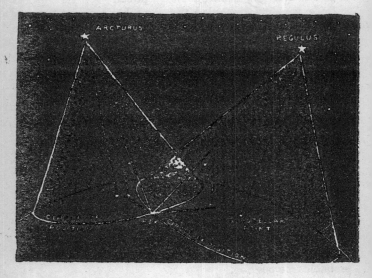

Once you grasp this ancient concept of the universe, celestial navigation becomes simple. Beneath every star at any given moment is a point on earth, as the Polynesian navigators well knew, and these substellar points move with their stars parallel to the lines of latitude, ever westward in a pattern so constant that its zodiacal forms of three thousand years ago are still recognizable today. You can find about fifty of the brighter stars thus listed in the air almanac, with their latitudes, and their longitudes in relation to Aries, the prime meridian of the sky, just as places on earth are listed in geography books in relation to the earth's prime meridian that runs through Greenwich, England.

Through Wind and Cloud

4

Ocean of the Sky

As THE AIRPLANE floated snugly in its dark fold of air I relaxed to my work with the confidence of thorough training. The mighty night wind moved by me like a shadow in a tunnel. I sensed the flecks of unseen cloud curving in to meet our wings, the mist slanting up to whet our blades.

It is quite easy to look upon the sky as a kind of greater ocean, the cities of Earth being on its sea floor looking up toward the nebulous surface somewhere above. If you think of the cirrus cloud level as the surface, and of birds and airplanes as fish swimming in these depths, the illusion is complete.

If we lived in the ocean of water we would drown. If we lived in the ocean of mud and earth and stone we would be buried. But instead we are in the third and highest ocean— the greatest of the three: the ocean of air.

The sky begins at our feet. We breathe it. We are actually crawling on the sea bottom of the heavens. We are the crabs of the airy depths.

But the sky ocean has its own distinctive qualities also. It is more primitive, elemental, and somehow fiercer than the earth below. In the sky you cannot stop: to stop is to die.

Even the helicopter and the hummingbird must spin and hover lest they fall. Even the balloon must drift with the wind, rising like a bubble, sinking like a sponge, moving as part of the volatile air itself—floating, drifting, gliding, sliding—ever given to the unseen power of air, air which is not the empty waste it seems but more ancient in its gaseousness, more vast and wild and wanton than anything the solid or liquid worlds ever knew.

Though we still use the expression "light as air," this is something of a deceptive phrase in view of the now known fact that the atmosphere of the earth is like a great drift of snow five hundred miles deep and weighing more than 5,000,000,000,000,000 tons. Gravity thus holds the airy sky to the earth with such a fierce hug that very few of its molecules can hope to escape. And besides packing plenty of weight the more tangible part of the earth's sky turns out to be rich in unseen substance. It is jam-packed with life and adventure, with collision and things beyond the dreams of seagulls and stewardesses. In an ounce of air there are more than 1,000,000,000,000,000,000,000,000 molecules boiling and moiling about, each pulsing with electron orbits, buttoned with mesons, figuratively bursting with excitement. Most of them might be visualized as occupying the shapes of cigars or dumbbells or eggs but so small and moving at such terrific speed that they are invisible even to an electron microscope.

Their violence of course is basic to the sky and actually makes it blue by scattering the correspondingly short light waves at the blue-violet end of the spectrum, while the longer, steadier red waves refuse to reflect back to our eyes.

Most of these molecules are named nitrogen or oxygen, elemental vibrant beings. A few are sleepy argon, lungy carbon dioxide, wet hydrogen, with an occasional odd duck of

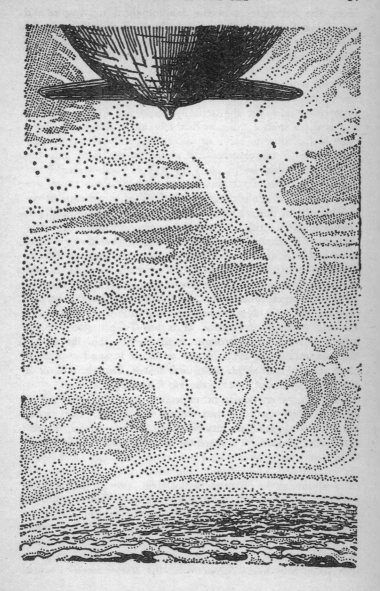

neon, krypton, helium, xenon, or pungent ozone out of the wake of lightning. They are much and sundry, these molecules of air, for air is not a chemical compound. It is a mixture of gases with a certain amount of solids and usually some liquid blended in and thoroughly stirred by the tireless spoon of wind. The solid part of the sky is called dust and is one of its vital ingredients. The housewife is not trained to approve of dust yet she actually could not live without it. Nor is there such a thing as dust-free air in nature. Without some sort of dust to serve as nuclei for condensation the sky would always be cloudless, it would never rain, and the earth would soon be parched for lack of fresh water. Even the tiny particles of salt dust tossed aloft by ocean waves are invaluable in condensing rain, which takes this means of returning salt to the sea refreshed with the wind's blessing.

One need not think of dust as necessarily dirty or something that needs to be cleaned up. The reverse may be true, for dust-laden air can be about as pure as anything else in this finite world and even has been used for soap. Air in fact has about as much purifying power as the sea, if less concentrated, and many a shirt gets more of a cleansing on the line than in the tub. Next time your hands are dirty just try washing them in air instead of water. Take a good strong breeze if there's one around: it dispatches the dirt faster. Mohammed taught his followers to wash in sand storms or plain sand or dust when water was scarce. Straight still air is slower in effect but will do the job if you give it time.

The viruses are kinds of molecules found everywhere in air, and their varieties and shapes are legion. They look, under the electron microscope, like string, caviar, beads, boats, and popcorn. They are the smallest, most elusive form of life, and bring to mankind epidemics, problems, and benefits mysterious. They usually reproduce their own kind, yet their mutations in offspring make them ever unpredictable, perhaps a tool of God to keep doctors and humanity unrutted in their thinking.

And there are the protozoa, more complex, higher creatures of the empty sky. Some of these are ancient prototypes of the airplane, having microscopic propellers which start to spin when they make contact with the starter force of moist

air. Humidity is their fuel. When they go dry these unicellu-
lar animals enclose themselves in hangarlike sheaths or cysts
and remain dormant in the dust—dust which is now part of
the earth, now caught up by the wind and blown around the
world, the life still within it, floating, flying, sleeping. When
at last the winged dust is dissolved in rain or water the cysts
open again, allowing the protozoa to emerge, awake, say
"contact," and resume their errant spinning lives—riding upward in the clouds, swimming downward in the rain.

Some of these creatures are fourteen-pointed stars, some
pulsing hexahedrons, some shaped like spaghetti, honey-
combs, doughnuts, pretzels, hourglasses, seahorses, roulette
wheels, pyramids, boomerangs—everything and more than
the molecules they are made of—some bubbles within bubbles, the inner bubbles the offspring of the outer, so that
when they grow to be as big as Mother they automatically
burst out of her to venture abroad on their own, minutes
later becoming bubble mothers themselves with new inner
bubble babies in their turn—thus, by inner-to-outer bubble
leapfrog, throbbing the generative rhythm of the sky.

No less remarkable among the air dwellers are the flying
lichen seedlings built of fungi and algae in the form of tiny
globular farms, the fungi farmers actually herding the algae
livestock on which they live, sometimes riding irregular
masses of inert dust for months on end, again blowing free,
intermittently changing in magnetic polarity, occasionally
getting doused in the floating droplet of a cloud.

Beyond such superficial details of air and moisture, science
has not yet illumined much of the hidden life of the upper
kingdom. Although air has been "duplicated" chemically in a
laboratory retort, no one so far has been able to make sky
life grow in artificial air until at least a tiny portion of natural air was added. The real sky thus still holds the secret of
life—a secret not difficult for it to keep while man knows
hardly the first thing about it.

As we go upward through the air's onion layers the temperature drops for a few miles. But then about eight miles
up it stops getting cooler and stays around 67° F. below
zero. That level where the temperature ceases falling is
known as the tropopause. It marks the bottom of the cold,

clear, cloudless part of the stratosphere, which is the stable level of future flight, the place where you can forget thunderstorms and turbulence and blind flying, the height where your flight plan practically ceases to be a gamble. The stratosphere, extending up to about sixty miles, includes a level around fifteen to twenty miles high so rich in ozone it is sometimes called the ozonosphere. By about thirty miles, because of ozone absorption of sun rays, the temperature has risen to $+170°$ F. There lies the land of twilight, which is really nothing but sunshine reflected off the scarce molecules of the upper sky at a reputed average height of thirty-seven miles.

Some fifteen miles higher comes the colder level where radio waves mysteriously begin to bounce fifty-odd miles back down to earth. All the atmosphere above this is called ionosphere, a strange hot, etheric habitat of meteors and auroras. This new outer skin of the onion is the earth's frontline insulation against the scorching blast of the sun and the never ending hail of charged particles and objects from outer space. Little is yet known of the ionosphere but the evidence is that it gets hotter again as you go farther from the earth out into our unseen sun shield.

Here there is so little air that it does not behave like air at all and temperature has a different meaning. The molecules of nitrogen and oxygen no longer bounce off one another every ten thousandth of an inch of their way, but move several feet between collisions. Any solid body in this giddy layer therefore can move at terrific speed almost without resistance, as if running through a room containing a couple of random bouncing pingpong balls instead of the familiar sea-level condition of air molecules packed solid to the ceiling like bricks.

The sky from the ionosphere looks black and the stars are brighter by day than you have ever seen them from earth by night. Looking down from up there the earth is strangely lighter in color than its surrounding sky, and so far below you that all the clouds seem to be lying belly to ground. The roundness of the planet is very apparent too, and details like cities and rivers usually invisible, while even great mountain ranges are scarcely discernible in the hazy depths. If few men have yet actually been up that high there is food for imagination aplenty in photographs snapped from rockets and satellites careering hundreds of miles above the earth, and sundry other evidence and practical comparisons.

It is perhaps a first glimpse of what the sky may hold in all directions, upward as well as downward—for up here there are worlds and worlds, and we are flying not by human flight plan alone. Our destinations are not only of the earth, our cargoes not wholly earthly goods.

Even as Thoreau with his plow in Concord, we fly a broader pathway than you see. Indeed where the off engine roars it is not: it is further off. And where the nigh blade turns it will not be, for it is nigher still.

5

The Wind

THE GREATEST CORRECTIONS I have had to make in my navigating are written in Aeolus' book, in a breezy trailing scrawl —carefree, whimsical, yet etched beyond recall. It is largely for the wind's sake that we carry an extra two or three hours' supply of fuel. And many's the time when it has held body to soul—more times than the weather prophet wants to hear.

What is the nature of this flighty spirit, the wind? Have ever men by any thrust of austromancy divined the secret of his being, his rule of life?

Men have tried since their first forest homes were uprooted by the tempest and their sea rafts battered by the squall, since the time of the flood when "God made a wind to pass over the earth, and the waters assuaged." Homer called the four winds by name: Boreas, the north wind, later immortalized in the Towers of the Winds at the Acropolis as a muffled-up old man with a conch to blow the bitter threnody of winter; Euros, the grizzled east wind, holding high his cloak to huff the storm: Notos, the virile south wind, emptying his jar of warm rain; and Zephyros, the beautiful young west wind, bearing fruits in his careless mantle.

The mountains of Thrace were the poetic home of these ancient Greek winds, whom Hesiod called "the children of the morning." Aeolus dwelt there in the howling wind tunnel of a cave which was his palace. He studied the heavens, invented the sail, and wore his billowing robes as the great moody god of all the winds of the earth. It was he who tied up in a bag and presented to Ulysses Boreas, Euros, and every wind that could blow his ship. When Ulysses' men untied the bag they unwittingly gave all the winds their irrevocable freedom.

Some of the legends of Aeolus are being repeated in real life today, for aerodynamic engineers again are locking up winds in wind tunnels large and small, training them to their bidding, sometimes torturing them. And weather officers are tying winds into packages so they can be put into bags (the flight bags of navigators) and carried out across the world. Even our wind-plotting instruments and computers for figuring the wind and catching its drift have a windy, Aeolian look about them these days, their wind-swept lines reminding me of graceful cirrus clouds: mare's-tails of calculus, mackerel mathematics.

And in the Aeolian tradition, surviving still among many peoples of the world, came many such aphorisms as "a heron flying from the sea and crying is a sign of wind," or "ducks foretell rain by diving, but wind by flapping their wings."

But what did the Greeks know of the wind's way? Was there more in wind than divine whim or mortal magic?

The prevailing theory of the philosophers was that the initial principle of wind is fire. Wasn't it an observable fact that the leaping flames sent forth their sparks and smoke and airy ashes on a hot draft upwards to the sky? Was it not clear also that such violent up-currents disturbed the air and, like fire itself, spread rapidly outwards? If so, then the wind must be a kind of flame of the atmosphere—a hidden air conflagration.

As the millenniums passed, new meteorologists and austromancers and prophets altered and added to wind lore. In medieval Germany the *luft-mensch* appeared, a man reputedly willing to "buy a bag of smoke, trade it for two bags of wind, and lose them both in a gale." In medieval Scotland the more progressive witches got to raising wind by dipping a rag in water and beating it thrice on a stone, chanting:

> *"I knok this rag upon this stane*
> *To raise the wind in the divellis name,*
> *It sall not lye till I please againe."*

The wind is kinder indeed than some of nature's mysterious forces, and has more often than not shown itself the friend of the wise. Cryptic it is to the pedestrian mind, but it freely offers clues of itself to the seer, the thinker, and the believer. As when the dry leaves fill the air of October or the winter wood smoke outlines his transparent being to our feeble eyes, so can perspective reveal something of the earth's total scheme of wind.

To see the whole, one must stand back in the sky a piece and view the full sphere, look well at its mountains and seas and at that faint envelope of air that wraps it round like cellophane about a pumpkin. It is plain to see that this globe has wanted neither fare nor favor, for its form is that of the intemperate friar or his gassy horse. It bulges at the waistline. And this is more true of the air than of land or sea.

There is more than one equator at the earth's fat middle,

you see. Beside the well-known fixed equator of rotation there is the moody heat equator which is the equator of the winds. Unlike the rigid former, familiar on every world map, the subtle equator of the winds drifts with the seasons and bends strangely about the continents and seas. It is known also as the doldrums, the famous belt of equatorial calms where olden sailing ships would drift for weeks with limp sails and blistering planks, "ghosting through." It is the band of greatest sun heat, where the warm air rises fastest, leaving a low-pressure girdle of lazy light air about the earth, forever bulging upward, forever sucking toward it the more temperate airs from north and south: the trade winds.

As the trade winds carry cooler air toward the wind equator, the air already there, warmed and rising, flows back northward and southward again at a higher level forming opposite and less-known antitrade winds.

At the poles a different sort of circulation holds sway, calm cooling air descending and fanning intermittently outwards in great bursts. The bursts do not move symmetrically from the poles, but in curving irregular waves of fingers, while warm air to replace the cold flows poleward between and above the fingers. And now again the pole of the winds is not the axis pole of earth's rotation for, as wind is thermodynamic air, the polar circulation naturally centers around the poles of cold—in Antarctica and Siberia.

Although the warm air in general flows toward the poles and the cool air toward the equator, the winds keeping a kind of balance of energy in the atmosphere, the total flux and flood of air is far from mannerly or simple. The warmed air in its poleward flow is not content to remain aloft as would seem reasonable. Instead it cools, contracts, increases in pressure, and presently descends to earth, meteorologically itching for trouble—behaving as only prescient nature could conscionably permit.

Great wreaths of this clear, heavy settling air are found girdling the subtropical earth north and south of the equator where the fitful Calms of Cancer and Capricorn prevail, commonly known as the horse latitudes. These zones have always rivaled the doldrums as a bane to shipping and are the breeding grounds of many of the world's strange winds.

Some say they were named after Ross, a British explorer. In German atlases Ross Latitudes appeared as *Ross Breiten*, but *Ross* is an old German word for horse and when retranslated into English they may mistakenly have become the horse latitudes.

Others insist they were named for the equestrian ghosts of ill-fated cargoes of the horse transports which much too often on voyages to the Indies found themselves helpless victims of calms or fickle variables, eventually having to dump their dead and dying horses overboard, a pathetic contribution to the nightmares of Davy Jones.

Beyond the horse latitudes on the pole sides lie cooler regions of swirling uneasy winds which blow predominantly from the west. In our northern hemisphere this broad sash of winds covering the United States and Europe and most of Asia is known as the prevailing westerlies and they are characterized by the shifting of the northward moving air which, approaching the earth's axis, speeds up like a shortened pendulum, racing eastward ahead of the turning earth.

In the south temperate zone the corresponding air currents are the "brave west winds" which sweep unobstructed by any land around the empty southern oceans encircling the whole earth. These are the motive force of the famous "graybeards," the grim waves thirty to fifty feet high that roll endlessly eastward off the Horn, around and around the gray, watery world.

It is written that the old-time whalers who battled those endless seas last century dubbed the successive southern latitudes: the roaring forties, the howling fifties, and the screeching sixties. Not without reason either: one of the outposts of the sixties, 1200 miles below Tasmania, Adelie Land, Antarctica, has recorded the world's most relentless winds, with an average velocity of more than fifty miles per hour day in day out the whole year round. Subzero Adelie gusts often measured around two hundred m.p.h. and it is understandable that Sir Douglas Mawson who wintered there early in the century was heard to mutter through his teeth on his homeward voyage that a long and happy life somewhere else could hardly make up for a single year spent in Adelie Land.

On the poleward edges of the westerlies, around latitude 45° N. and 50° S., are the great mixing belts where warmed humid air from the tropics meets clear polar bear's breath from the poles in wavy shifting "polar fronts" of variable and veering winds. These zones cover the northern United States and most of Europe and well account for the fickle moody weather familiar to so much of the world's population. Beyond them: the comparative quiet of the arctic and antarctic.

Have you heard the wind names of the world, which are among the least known and most beautiful of words? They are truly the heritage of all men for they reflect the tongues of history from ancient Cathay to the slang of the United States Army. Consider the dry khamsin of Egypt, reputed to blow sand unceasingly for fifty days; the westerly datoo of the Straits of Gibraltar; the misty waimea of Hawaii; the cool pontias from the Rhone gorges; the chinook of the dry American plains; the sudden violent williwaw of Alaska and Magellan's Strait; the biting black buran of Russia; the great typhoon of the China Sea; the whispering matsukaze which shifts through Japanese pine groves; the mild shamal that descends the twin valleys of the Tigris and Euphrates; the warm brickfelder of southern Australia; the playful vento coado which whistles through crannies in the hillside hovels of Portugal; the snorting sonora which crosses Arizona from Mexico to California each summer; the dainty feh of Shanghai; the whirling tsumuji of Japan; the vindictive rok of Iceland; the refreshing imbat off the blue Mediterranean; the ruthless helm wind of Cumberland which uproots turnips in the field.

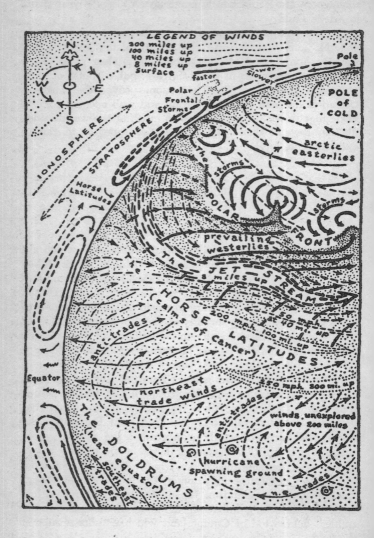

The mightiest of winds, the great West Indian hurricane (from the Taino word "huracan" or "evil spirit"), dominates the Caribbean as the typhoon (from "ty fung," "great wind") the China Seas. Most of the true tropical hurricanes are born mysteriously and unattended in the giddy heat of the doldrums. Little is definitely yet proved about the dynamics of their origin. But their initial power is widely conjectured to come from a rising vortex of heat over water that "must be at least 82° F." and surrounded by a certain amount of atmospheric instability.

Hurricanes are mainly a late-summer phenomenon, and this suggests that the instability associated with them is derived from the cumulative effect of the sun's nearly vertical rays throughout the summer. When air begins to rise in any area the surrounding air must move inward to replace that which has risen and unless it is almost exactly at the equator it is bound to acquire some rotation from the effect of the turning earth. As it rushes inward it inevitably spins faster like a shortened pendulum, taking on more and more of the characteristics of a young hurricane.

In bygone times sailors had great superstitions about this fearful incurving of the wind which was sometimes strong enough to send ships sailing in circles day after day. Usually the vortex dies out again before too long, but near the time of the autumnal equinox in the Caribbean when the heat has attained its peak one occasionally becomes a monster of violence.

The first visible signs of warning in the sky are gay streamers of high cirrus clouds, usually radiating from one point on the southeastern horizon, followed by a thickening hood of milky cirro-stratus, perhaps revealing a halo around the sun or moon; then grayer and lower clouds, alto-stratus, alto-cumulus, darkening, sometimes turning to copper in color, with dense ragged clouds scudding low overhead in a different direction from the higher ones.

The finale of this ominous overture is a heavy black wall of cumulo-nimbus, closing down from above like a curtain of doom. Sometimes it is called the bar cloud, approaching in

the form of a massive bar from two to five miles up, and extending as far as the eye can see—while just before it the visibility is crystal clear, and the trade wind gives way to fitful scherzo breezes.

The passage of the bar itself leaves no mistake that it is the start of the hurricane proper, for violent squalls now begin and lashing rain increases in a moody intermittent rhythm as successive armlike banks of clouds march overhead, sometimes ten minutes apart, sometimes more than an hour, with violent thunder squalls often punctuating the spells of howling mist-strewn gales.

Seen by a hurricane scout flying at 50,000 feet, the great sprawling disturbance would look like a series of concentric cumulus mountain chains, peaked with towering thunderheads—each rising higher than the last as he approaches the dramatic center of the system. The valleys are sometimes so deep and dark they seem to extend down under the sea but are really miles above the worst squalls, for the soaring ridges can rise as high as ten and twelve miles, possibly higher if we only had sufficient records to know.

Of course even a pilot in the stratosphere could hardly see all of a mature hurricane, which might be four or five hundred miles in diameter, but if he were thirty miles higher in a rocket he could undoubtedly take in the whole, noticing the spiral pattern of the encircling thundery ridges that spread further apart and get more irregular as they reach outward from the center, finally dissipating into ragged patches and dainty streaks of cirrus perhaps two hundred and fifty miles out.

The central eye is plainly the most fascinating hurricane part, being often a bowl of clear blue sky 25 miles in diameter reaching right down to the sea. Intense young hurricanes may have little eyes only three or four miles across, but the average eye diameter is fourteen miles and in many cases covered with a white eyelid of broken or solid strato-cumulus blanketing the surface at an altitude of a few thousand feet while the spiral thunder ridges rise all around it like tiers of a Roman amphitheatre.

The heat of the eye is usually quite noticeable even at low altitudes and its center has been found to be as much as 32° F. warmer than the outer storm at 18,000 feet. The eye's calm is proverbial but so real that flocks of sea birds have been seen there on several occasions, wheeling end-

lessly and understandably anxious to keep out of the encircling fury as long as they are able. Airplanes can fly there with relative safety too, but surface ships avoid the eye with well-founded dread, preferring the areas of swiftest wind.

For the surrounding hundred-mile blasts blow the waves top-less and decimate the crested seas to reasonable, truncated proportions, while in the eye the great swells and waves seem to run wantonly, beyond control or order, often clash-ing from opposite directions in such wild collisions as to rear up jagged pyramids of water high enough to buckle a 10,000-ton ship in two or stave in her decks by toppling upon them.

The extreme low pressure near the center of a hurricane, by the way, causes the sea level to be sucked up abnormally high under it, especially on its dangerous side of forward spin (the right side of a hurricane north of the equator). This elevation of several feet, furiously lashed by the winds around it, builds up a heavy swell which may travel as fast as eighty miles an hour, outrunning the storm itself and some-times even its remotest barometric indications—the dog be-fore his master. Though such a swell can be dangerous when it arrives at high tide, at least it forewarns of something even more dangerous to follow.

The unblinking clarity of the hurricane eye is a distinctive feature not often visible in the smaller vortex storms, and to many of us who have never seen a hurricane eye to eye, its full significance requires an effort of appreciation. The eye's deceptiveness, for example, is a clue as to why the Tainos named this wind the "Evil Spirit"—for the low-pressure calm-ness in the center of the fury often leads the uninitiated to assume the whole hurricane has passed—to their undoing.

On September 18, 1926, when a hurricane whirled spang through Miami, everybody huddled in the safest spots, espe-cially during the wild pre-dawn hours of hundred-mile east-erly winds just before the eye. When it suddenly grew dead calm and a beautiful sunrise appeared, hundreds of people came out to go to work or to see the night's devastation. Scores of adventurous young people crossed the long cause-way to Miami Beach for the thrill of swimming in the great surf. But after only an hour of lull, an abrupt opposite gale from the west arose, reaching full hurricane force so quickly that the surge of water out of Biscayne Bay washed over the causeway, sweeping many astonished bathers to their deaths.

Miami Beach virtually disappeared under the rising wind-whipped tide, drowning additional hundreds.

There are nearly always some such storms meandering about the world's oceans, like the almost unannounced typhoon that flattened Wake Island just after I last flew there in 1952, or the baguio (Philippine hurricane) that in 1927 made the lowest barometric reading ever officially accepted: 26.185 inches.

Several have left their mark on history too—perhaps never more dramatically than when Kublai Khan's fleet set sail from the Asiatic mainland in A.D. 1281 to invade Japan. There appears little doubt that the then primitive Japanese would have fallen easy prey to the Golden Horde, which had conquered the world from the Mediterranean to the China Sea, had it not been for a great typhoon (called *kamikaze* or "divine wind" by the Japanese) which swept without warning upon the overloaded wooden transports, scattering and foundering them to an almost total loss. After this single awe-inspiring blow from Fujin, the wind god, the great Khan lost all appetite for pressing his designs on the Land of the Rising Sun.

Strange to relate, Fujin arose again in Japan's defense in mid-December 1944 and actually gave her a modern naval victory about as devastating (if not so decisive) as the triumph of 1281. When Admiral Halsey's Third Fleet retired from striking Mindoro to refuel five hundred miles eastward in the Pacific, such huge seas came up that all oil lines broke before fuel could be pumped through them. Nor had Navy weather officers sufficient information to locate the typhoon's center or course in time, and it struck Halsey with full ferocity, sinking three U.S. ships and damaging twenty-eight others, demolishing or blowing overboard 146 planes, killing 790 men, and forcing a long postponement of the then-planned American invasion of Luzon.

Devastating as is the hurricane in its vast strength, how-

ever, it is far behind the tiny tornado in concentrated velocity. Named from the Latin *tornare*, "to turn," and variously
described by Pliny the Elder, Seneca, and Lucretius, this
frenzied whirlwind plays hornet to the hurricane's elephant. It
has its corresponding local names from the *tourbillon* of
France to the *piao* of China, its waterspout variants from the
dancing *trompa* of the Black Sea to the descriptive *sky-
pompe* of the Baltic.

While the hurricane, cutting a swath two or three hundred miles wide and sometimes ten thousand miles long during its fortnight to a month of rampage, blows with a velocity known to have exceeded 200 m.p.h. at its highest fury,
the little tornado's path is rarely as much as half a mile
wide, usually less than a couple of dozen miles long, and it
seldom outlives the hour. Yet the air whizzing around the
tornado's vacuous center moves with a speed estimated at
from 200 to 800 m.p.h. More accurate determination of tornado velocity has not been made at this writing, for the
good reason that on the rare occasions when anemometers
have happened to be in its path, they have been wrecked by
the wind itself—committing a kind of meteorological suicide.

Thunderstorm weather is ideal for tornado breeding, with
violent heat rivers bearing the air upward like a giant drain
in reverse, the black thunderheads serving as the inverted
bottom of the tropospheric bathtub out of which the air is
being sucked aloft in a swirling effusion. Thus the part of a
tornado hidden in the clouds is immense as compared to its
visible trunk and the great twister that smashed through
Worcester, Massachusetts, in 1953 was fourteen miles high
at the cirrus top of its overriding thunderhead.

A tornado measures up to a hurricane in more than
height, however, as is shown by the fact that its funnel also
has an eye at its center which, in rare cases, has been known
to exceed a mile in diameter. And, as in a hurricane, this is
the calmest part of the tornado. Even the tall surrounding
funnel is not so much to be feared as the faster wind whirling around its base, the tornado's outer collar that is usually
black with raised dust and in which debris is continuously

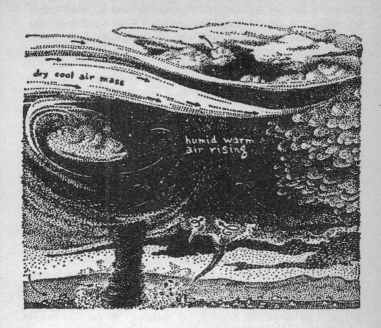

being sucked aloft, then inevitably hurled outward again in a wild fountain of nigritude.

Most witnesses of tornadoes do not remember them as having any particular smell other than that of the raised dust, yet a few reliable and sensitive observers have reported a distinct odor of sulphur and ozone—perhaps the chemical consequences of vacuous air and electrical discharge. Certainly tornadoes are associated with a special lightning of very delicate lacelike texture and of almost continuous flickering frequency. Pilots flying blind through thunderstorms have been known to take evasive action after recognizing this tornadic trademark, usually climbing above 15,000 feet to avoid the risk of running into a hidden vortex at its level of greatest frenzy.

What can happen in a blind collision between an airliner and a tornado ambushed in a cloud is suggested by the fate of the DC-6 that is thought to have run into a "stormspout" off Mobile, Alabama, on February 14, 1953. All that is definitely known is that the big plane was suddenly and mysteriously thrown out of control and spun or dove into the Gulf, killing all forty-six persons aboard.

As to the sound of a tornado, the memories of all witnesses are usually quite definite. It has the roar of a thousand trains passing in the night. If more distant, the prolonged whine of a swarm of bees. Even from twenty-five miles away, the persistent bellow of a mature tornado has been noticed, and for as long as an hour before the storm's arrival, keen ears have warned a population of the danger. The final roar is frequently augmented by nearly continuous thunder and often as not by a rattling obbligato of large hail mixed with shingles, nails, and assorted splintering boards.

The average recorded duration of the tornado's passage over one spot is but 15 seconds, and its average total endurance along the ground about 8 minutes. But many tornadoes are far from average. One midwestern twister was recorded as dawdling along in a continuous path for "seven hours." Although the average swath cut by tornadoes, according to statistics, is thirteen miles long, this amazing storm started in Missouri at noon and meandered eastward across the middle of Illinois and southern Indiana, stopping only at sunset close to the Ohio border, having traveled 293 miles, "the longest continuous path of a tornado of which there is any authentic record." An unusual but not unique feature of this one also was that no funnel of any sort was visible after the first hour, but just "a boiling mass of clouds" in which individual clouds "seemed to roll towards each other and downward, like the meshing of a pair of huge cogwheels," no doubt sucked inward by the central vortex hidden somewhere in the very low cumulo-nimbus confusion.

The element of personal whimsy is proverbial with tornadoes in the way they will pick out one house yet leave the next untouched, or whisk one member of a family into the sky like magic, perhaps carry a cupboard full of crockery for a quarter of a mile and set it down without breaking a dish.

One twister whooshed a horse into the air among debris, horse flies, horse shoes and barn, allowing the terrified animal to alight unharmed half a mile distant. In another case a woman milking a cow saw the cow swept into a black funnel, leaving her sitting with a pail—but no cow. At Harleyville, Kansas, a whirler passing close to a farmhouse sucked the bedding and mattress from under a sleeping boy without so much as giving him a scratch. Another blew a lighted kerosene lamp for several hundred yards, leaving it still burning and undamaged though with a smoky chimney.

An exceptional account of tornadic violence as viewed from the sky is the report of an Air Force lieutenant who happened to be flying over Waco, Texas, when that city of 90,000 people was struck on May 11, 1953. As the twister bore down Main Street, he saw plate-glass windows on both sides burst outward into the street in progressive waves, then opposing brick walls met each other as they crashed on top of the lanes of slow-moving cars, roofs falling into the wall-less interiors of the stores. A theater and a six-story furniture mart burst at the seams like slow bombs, both immediately collapsing into twisted heaps of wreckage.

The explosive tendency of an enclosed building when enveloped in a tornado vortex is obviously the result of the sudden decrease in pressure outside the building relative to its normal interior atmosphere of about fifteen pounds per square inch. When the barometer drops to twenty-three inches, as was unofficially recorded for the U.S. Weather Bureau in the eye of a tornado at Minneapolis on August 20, 1904, the pressure inside a closed house suddenly finds itself almost four pounds per square inch higher than outside. That means that the force of a ton is immediately exerted against every section of wall two feet square, several tons upon an average window, and nearly a thousand tons throughout the typical small house.

Although a good deal has been discovered recently about tornadoes, man has not learned to outwit them. In fact their nature seems to have the curious effect of making them increasingly dangerous and destructive as populations grow. This seems to be because cities are a tornado's natural prey, and effective warning systems very difficult to organize, even though progress is being made in detection of sferics in the atmosphere generated by the lacy tornadic lightning and a new barometer alarm has been designed to be triggered by the "pressure jump" that often precedes a tornado. People in general have not yet been trained for tornado action. Those who would telephone an alarm of fire forget to give the more important (and more unselfish) alarm of tornado, and the storm wreaks its worst havoc in cities where anyone caught in the streets is in mortal danger of being buried under flying debris. This is in striking contrast with hurricanes, which are mainly maritime, are progressively being disarmed through systems of warnings several days ahead (including a new balloon that automatically floats in a hurricane's eye and continuously broadcasts its position), and which in any case seldom develop the wind force for collapsing buildings more substantial than light hangars, barns, and cottages.

The dust devil can be distinguished from the tornado mainly by its smaller size and by the fact that it is dancing upon the earth rather than hanging from a cloud. To a meteorologist it is the trunk without the elephant.

Nonetheless, these small vortexes of sand are a common sight on the desert, and derive their power from updrafts of sun-baked air caught in natural eddies of the wind. Their average height has been estimated as 600 feet, maximum diameter about 100 feet, and they seldom last an hour. The biggest one on record was seen on the Egyptian desert near Cairo. It stood a mile high, and spun along for five and a half hours, obeying the general rule of thumb that a dust devil will stay alive as many hours as it has thousands of feet in altitude. The Egyptians call this wind the Zobaa.

When the surrounding wind fields are turbulent, dust devils often contort themselves into curves, corkscrews or leaning angular figures, sometimes scores of them in one apparently co-ordinated ballet. In California there is a kind called the "towel rack roll" because it rolls nearly horizontally, shaped like a towel rack, with both ends turned to the ground. Others are egg-shaped, spherical or even down-blowing with a doughnut-shaped cloud of rolling dust. Large vertical ones tend to have six counter-rotating eddies spinning all around them.

The most epic whirlwind in history, I believe, was the one that miraculously arose during Mohammed's first battle in the little valley of Badr near Medina in A.D. 624. Awakening from a brief spiritual trance just at the critical turn of the fighting, Mohammed impulsively picked up a handful of dirt and flung it toward his enemies with a holy curse. Whether or not he intended literal fulfillment of the ancient prophecy that he who sows the wind shall reap the whirlwind, he mounted a horse and charged like a madman into the midst of the fray, followed by a very small dust devil that had curiously sprung to life from his cast handful of earth. As the wrathful prophet dashed forward it is said that the whirling spiral of dust behind him grew rapidly in size and speed until it drew abreast of Mohammed and swept with full fury into the masses of Koreishite swordsmen opposing him. In a few minutes the enemy were so blinded and confused by the unexpected storm that most of them turned in headlong retreat and the first Moslem victory was assured.

Waterspouts are basically similar to tornadoes and dust devils, yet have a cleaner, smoother look both because of the dearth of dust at sea and the seascape's relative lack of friction. They also depend proportionately more on humidity for power, less on heat.

The commonest kind are what weather men call "storm spouts" or maritime tornadoes which, like all tornadoes, have their roots in cumulo-nimbus clouds. They often come in flocks. One ship saw thirty big ones in one day. The Gulf knows many of them in summer and they appear on the Great Lakes and most of the tropic and not-too-temperate seas. They often turn out when the sky is sultry and sullen, when there may be a bluish haze and surface suggestions of the moodier air currents. Suddenly a dark elephantine cloud with a hanging trunk is noticed, usually lengthening rapidly from the stubby tornadic funnel to the scrawnier, snakelike stem of the typical waterspout.

In most cases you can look right through the transparent bole of the vortex as it dips down to draw up what superheated air and spray it can collect just over the water. But it has enough condensed moisture to be not invisible, and occasionally even appears with an outer cylinder of falling mist descending around it like a fountain after being lifted in the inner whirl.

The most recently discovered of the world's important winds is a gigantic, elusive torrent of thin air that howls perpetually around the base of the stratosphere somewhere eight miles above the middle latitudes. It is shaped like a tape worm, follows the course of a shaken rope, and moves invisibly at a speed varying from 100 to 500 m.p.h.

Respectfully known as the jet stream, it is really a double whirlwind nearly as much bigger than the hurricane, as the hurricane is bigger than the tornado. In fact, each of the earth's two jet streams averages about 22,000 miles in circumference, and the Arctic and Antarctic circles form but the irises of their oppositely staring eyes, one looking perpetually at the North Star, the other gazing forever upon the Southern Cross.

Almost too tremendous for human conception, this lofty wind was first suspected by the navigators of the B–29 bombers flying to southern Japan near the end of World War II. The flight crews were amazed to find that north of the horse latitudes at 35,000 feet, they regularly met west winds of more than 250 m.p.h., three times as swift as the average hurricane. Sometimes they found themselves actually flying backwards at 40,000 feet in 400-m.p.h. headwinds! They could not account for it nor find even a mention of it in the meteorology books. When the weather engineers heard the reports and collected all the information at hand, it was evident that something big was up. An entirely new kind of wind had been discovered, a sort of by-product of the age of jet, a supercharged Gulf Stream of the upper sky.

Special projects of exploration were immediately launched to investigate it thoroughly. This was not easy, for an invisible river eight miles straight up is something even the Air Force was not organized to handle, especially when its unknown course is constantly shifting both horizontally and vertically, sometimes by as much as a thousand miles in a day.

The jet stream is shaped just as a river is supposed to be, wide and relatively shallow. But besides being a hundred times faster, it is also a hundred times bigger than any river you ever saw on earth, far bigger even than the Gulf Stream which would exceed all the continental rivers put together. Thus the jet stream of air is by all odds the world's greatest river—a twin river flowing continuously sometimes for nearly twenty-five thousand miles around each hemisphere, only a few miles deep but its volume amounting to five thousand cubic miles of air per minute past every point on its banks (if it had any banks)—its total course in both hemispheres: more than forty-five thousand miles, or a fifth of the way to the moon.

The jet stream has also a rhythmic wave motion which sometimes follows the phases of the moon with an almost feminine fatality. Its cyclic month or longer starts with a straight west wind that very gradually begins to undulate in the manner of a snake coming out of hibernation. After ten days of continuous increase in amplitude, the wave curves are describing moving S shapes two or three thousand miles apart that presently develop signs of instability, actually breaking apart by the end of the second or third week into loose wheels and kidney whorls that fly off as separate circulations and may roll on, for all now known, as far as the equator and the poles.

After a wild week of such wanton discontinuity, the discordant waves have usually canceled each other out enough

JET STREAM PROGRESSIONS

to permit new frontal pressures to oil the turbulence. Thus the trend turns again toward order and in another week the jet stream has notably ironed out its curves so it can stiffen back into the simple western component of its beginning.

Naturally this great wind offers wonderful possibilities for saving time and fuel on long easterly flights—especially where it has been rechecked as most virile in winter off southern Japan, over the southeastern United States, and in the clear skies of Egypt and Arabia.

Such interesting problems in calculus as to how far it is worthwhile to go out of one's way in pursuit of the jet stream, how late in the spring it can be used despite the seasonal slump, exactly where the efficient navigator should cut into it or veer out for his optimum course—these will occupy our minds in the coming years and should well fill the gap left by the tedious spherical trigonometry of old.

The murderous bomb wind, born of the atomic age, is one of the strangest of all the world's winds. Even with the earliest "model T" atomic bombs the outward blast at a thousand feet from "zero" (directly under the bomb) blows at 800 m.p.h., or faster than sound. Two miles away the wind is still whooshing out at 70 m.p.h. But this vast expanding puff is exhausted in a couple of seconds and is followed by an instant of stillness as in the eye of a hurricane. Then immediately it reverses itself, the wind literally bouncing back into the vacuum at about half its outward velocity but lasting longer. This double-action wind is what causes most structural damage in an atomic explosion, and many buildings which are only weakened by the initial outward blow are collapsed by the rebounding blast. H-bomb winds and bigger and worse blasts from successively more powerful explosions can be expected to behave in similar patterns but with velocities and distances proportionately increased.

And don't imagine that winds are only out there in the sky or blown by special instruments. Winds are everywhere. Winds are moving air. That draft down the hall—that's a wind. The sneeze. That's a wind. That rise of warmth over the stove. That's the kid brother of the same wind that starts thunderstorms to growling. Some have names. Some have not. But in God's eye every one is a wind, however small— and any one of them somehow may grow into a whirlwind, even as the handful of dust that Mohammed threw at Badr.

Another wind discovery of importance was the vast tropospheric scope of our traffic rule: keep to the right. When you are flying around a thunderstorm or a tornado it may be the difference between life and death to go right instead of left. To right you're with the wind, to left against it. This is because all storms and low pressure areas in the northern hemisphere are surrounded by counterclockwise winds. The cause is the motion of the earth itself: the veering geostrophic, gyroscopic force known as coriolis. It is the reason why an east wind spells trouble, being part of a storm from the west. It is why the right side of a north-moving hurricane is the dangerous side of forward spin. It is why an airplane flying east (turning faster than the earth) is lighter than the same airplane flying west, or why an airplane flying over the equator (where centrifugal force is greatest) is lighter than one flying elsewhere. It is why a pendulum clock, taken to a northern country, will run fast. It is the secret of the gyroscopic compass: the ever present centrifugal component of net gravity.

A mighty planetary force is obviously at work here, causing everything from spinning tops to draining bathtubs to turn one way more easily than the other in each hemisphere. This is because the earth beneath the sky is forever turning "out from under" whatever is upon it, whether air or water or solid moving object. It is why arctic rivers cut faster into their right banks than their left ones, why the Trans-Siberian Railroad has to replace more right than left rails on each stretch of one-way track. It is why the German's Big Bertha gun in World War I, firing on Paris from seventy miles away, had to aim a mile to the left of target so the three-minute trajectory of its shells would be corrected. It is why a rocket missile aimed at New York today from the North Pole would, unless artificially guided en route, land near Chicago after an hour's flight. It is because the earth is constantly moving Chicago to where New York was an hour ago.

Could this also be why our northern merry-go-rounds turn counterclockwise, and our horse races and auto races counterclockwise around the track? Is it the reason why timber wolves in the north usually range counterclockwise around the territory they claim as theirs? Does it affect also pirouetting ballerinas, whirling dervishes, the spin of boomerangs, cowboys' lassos, circling seagulls, roulette wheels, and lazy Susans? Does it subconsciously influence you when you take a turn around the block?

With its almost timeless devotion, the wind has shaped and colored much of the earth—and the task continues hourly. Wind deposits called loess or eolation blanket wide areas of the continents and the sea bottoms. Wind erosion carves lofty rocks and lowly knolls, small swales of grass and rolling dunes that creep like waves in largo.

One such wave of sand swallowed the whole village of Kunzen on the Baltic, then in a few years flowed on to uncover it again—leaving it little the worse for wear. Yet in the

Sudan a sand haboob is known to have rasped down wooden telegraph poles in a night, and roughened windowpanes to intransparency in an hour.

Inexplicable indeed the moods and deeds of the wind, countless the mountain trees warped to its will, the whistling towers, the chimneys of stone sculpted by its sightless chisel, the buttes and the graceful monoliths. Atolls in the Pacific are said to be designed entirely by the steadfast tradewinds. Even the scope of great windward rain jungles in the tropics are architectured by the wind, and vast leeward deserts across Africa, Australia, Asia, and the Americas.

In May 1937 during a southwest gale yellow sand fell in Canton Basle, Switzerland, so heavily that the countryside appeared swathed in a strange sulphuric fog. The sand was later proved to be from the Sahara Desert a thousand miles away and it must have been picked up by a simoom to be blown over the Alps at above 12,000 feet.

At the same time in the Engadine valley, also in Switzerland, a mysterious fall of red sand occurred, the origin of which has not yet been discovered. At other times and places pebbles, shells, and seaweed, even living frogs and fishes, have rained upon the earth, perhaps after being sucked aloft in the vortex, then carried inexplicably on the wind for great distances.

Can anyone ever say what shall not serve as grist for the wind?

In Ireland they say that of all the barnyard creatures the pig is the most gifted for he alone can see the wind. If it's true, pilots should not stint on their breakfast bacon, even before a stratosphere flight, for you really have to see the wind to fly well. You have to think wind too, and feel it as a bird feels it on his wings and through the barbules of his feathers.

As you fly, the wind comes to you little by little, more every day, every week, depending on how sensitive you are. Little clues appear everywhere: that nodding tree down there with the leaves always lighter on the windward side, that dust behind the wagon, the rippling grass, the flag, the little waves on the lake. The whole air becomes at last a

fluid mass that you can see moving, that you can understand and trust and lean against. Your wings now grip it surely and hold you steadfast in the sky as firmly as your feet hold you above the ground.

No longer need you find yourself in the bone-chilling situation of a young lady pilot I know who hadn't learned to know the wind. Flying cross country in a small plane she saw ahead of her a range of hills and a dark cloud about two hundred feet above it. Thinking to pass easily between the hills and the cloud she continued dreamily on her course at an altitude slightly higher than the hills. It simply didn't occur to her to consider the wind. When she noticed that the plane was settling she just advanced the throttle and pulled into a climb to regain altitude. But for some reason, instead of rising the plane continued to settle. The girl naturally kept advancing the throttle, still trying to climb over the hill which didn't yet seem too much to her.

By the time she realized that the nearer she was getting to the hill the faster the plane was settling, it was too late to turn back. The situation suddenly looked hopeless. She was headed straight for a rocky ledge just below the top and she braced herself for the crash. But in the final instant an amazing wind hit her, supporting the plane so firmly that she neatly cleared the ridge and no sooner passed it than a violent upsurge lifted her high into the sky.

The close call left the girl shaky for days but she had learned a lesson she never forgot: there has to be a downdraft somewhere on the lee side of a hill. Observation will soon show where it is, and it is elementary in flying to know whether you are going with or against the wind and which is the lee side of any elevation.

A famous illustration of the consequences of not thoroughly learning this lesson is the tragic crash of the British dirigible R101. Seven hundred and seventy-five feet long, the R101 was in her day the largest airship in the world. She had taken off from Cardington, Britain, the afternoon of October 4, 1930, on her maiden voyage, bound for Egypt and the Orient with most of England's leading airmen on board. Considered, like the *Titanic*, the latest thing in comfort and safety, there was no quiver or qualm among the eager and prominent passengers who filed up her gangway only seven hours before the unimagined holocaust in a French sugarbeet field. Most of them had relaxed in the wide cabin for a smoke after dinner while cruising at sixty knots across the south coast and all retired early as the luxurious sky giant hummed reassuringly over the channel.

Above France the airship ran into a severe storm with high winds and savage rain. Suddenly, near Beauvais, her nose dipped steeply. Then the craft levelled somewhat for a few seconds before diving again, striking the ground and exploding into flame.

Fire shot through the entire length of the R101, and the bewildered passengers screamed in agony as they fought to escape the confusion of bedclothes, scorching heat, and smoke while flames leaped hundreds of feet above them, feeding on twenty-five tons of fuel oil as well as the huge mass of hydrogen. Only eight of the fifty-four persons managed to get out, each by his individual miracle—such as being doused under the water ballast tank, blown out of a window, diving through a fire-rent hole in the hull.

The pilot and navigator were both lost and none of the

survivors could explain what had caused the airship to dive. Four of them were crewmen who had been on duty in the two engine rooms where the engines were last seen "turning to perfection" and all mechanical equipment apparently in good order. Examination of the wreckage confirmed the fact that the elevators were (as they should have been) at the position for maximum nose lift.

The committee of investigation at first largely blamed the rain for the accident, though it was admittedly something of a mystery why the fast-moving airship could not have overcome the slight added weight of the downpour. Many months were to pass before some sleuth finally tracked down the real guilty element: the wind.

For in truth the culprit was one of those air falls or down-blowing eddies over the lee slope of a hill. The particular hill was about 500 feet high, near Beauvais, and the configuration of the ground there was found to affect the air up to a height of nearly 2000 feet. Although the minimum safe altitude for dirigibles had been declared to be two and one half times their length, or about 1900 feet for the R101, the great airship had approached Beauvais at only 1500 feet of altitude.

Obviously that had seemed safe enough to the pilot but, even though he was foreman and engineer of the Royal Airship Works, admittedly he had not sufficiently reckoned on the wind. Caught suddenly by her nose in the treacherous downdraft, the R101 tilted earthward. Some free hydrogen in her huge envelope floated aft to the stern, giving it so much lift that although her elevators were put up at once she could not answer but plunged helplessly to her doom.

Yet it is possible, with knowledge and care, to avoid going against the wind's grain. It can be profitable too, for there is an ancient saying that "the wind is not in your debt though it fill your sail." The flying navigator is therefore always seeking ways to cash in on his wind acquaintanceship, to fill his sail for nothing.

One of his newest ways (besides the sporadic jet stream) is pressure-pattern flying. In the early World War II days we used to fly by the great circle as ocean steamers do. That is the shortest geographical distance across the earth's curved surface. But now again we have found it worthwhile to go out of our way looking for favorable winds, as did the sailing ships, and on a daily routine basis. By going a hundred miles off the great circle we can sometimes get such a wind boost that we arrive an hour earlier. Some days we gain almost nothing. But in the long run it averages out. As it costs more than $1000 an hour to fly a modern four-engined airplane it is big money in the pocket to put a steady average following breeze on the payroll along with the crew.

Dr. Hugo Eckener of the *Graf Zeppelin* first proved this. The old *Graf* naturally couldn't fly very fast: perhaps seventy m.p.h. at cruising speed. On his westward crossing of the Atlantic if he had stubbornly tried to buck westerly headwinds he might have spent days going backward. Instead he closely studied pressure and wind conditions and zigzagged all over the ocean, hitchhiking on tail winds wherever they could be reached on time. He went extra miles over the water, but less miles through the air: a vitally important saving.

An important advance was made when navigators learned how to correct their barometers accurately for altitude so that they can tell whether they are approaching a lower pressure area or higher pressure, therefore whether the best winds are to the right or the left. Coming into lower pressure north of the equator you must of course veer to the right to find tail winds, as coming into higher pressure you turn to the left.

If you want to learn the most intimate of all the secrets of the wind you must take up gliding. For in a glider or sail plane every movement—often your life—depends on the wind.

Even better would be to become a bird. Prince of the soaring birds is the albatross—that wandering ghost of the

nether seas who is so truly the wind's child that he cannot even fold his great wings comfortably but, after an hour on the mast, must slump back into the sky again, like a club man into an armchair, in order to relax.

If there is another of God's creatures so attuned to the wind's world it must be the tiny gossamer spider whose web is almost the very essence of wind. More trusting than the able albatross, he throws his pliant being literally to the winds to do with what they will, retaining not even a free balloonist's control over the ups or downs of fate.

Did you ever see a gossamer spider on an October afternoon, standing on a tree limb or a gatepost preparing for take-off? With his tiny head to windward he spins out into the sky a fine silken thread from the spinneret at the end of his body. It's a "run-up" of a special kind. When this spider spinnaker is long enough to hold some real wind and he feels the halyard tugging hard, the spider lets go and sails away on the breeze.

Where to? That is a matter for the wind to decide. However, the gossamer spider has his slight measure of control. If the wind rises he can reef in his thread to "shorten sail." If the wind drops he can pay it out again like a yachtsman in a tight race. His own body is his craft and crew. He may sail thus on the wind for hundreds of miles, even across continents or seas if the wind wills it so, rising as high as 60,000 feet and remaining aloft for weeks. In proportion to his size he can cruise to the moon with ease, literally riding on a cushion of molecules tuned to the inscrutable marrow of the sky.

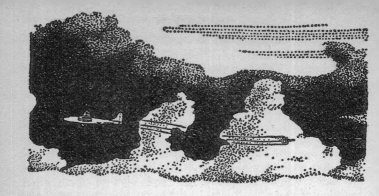

6

The Cloud

PERHAPS IT IS the sheer exuberance of the moving shapes I see from my work window up here. Or perhaps it is what naturally happens to thoughts that have too long been grazing in the pasture of the clouds. But every now and then I think I sense a maidenly wile in the way some passing nimbus form waves at us as we thunder by—our four engines coolly roaring.

Or maybe it is some trick of the turbulent wind which seems able to penetrate the densest cloud like a thought entering the mind, possibly bearing the same relation to it as the soul to the body. For indeed if the wind is the spirit of the sky's ocean, I say the clouds are its texture. They are embodied imagination, the sheet music of the heavens, the architecture of moving air. Theirs is easily the most uninhibited dominion of the earth. Nothing in physical shape is too fantastic for them. They can be round as apples or as fine as string, as dense as a jungle, as wispy as a whiff of down, as mild as puddle water, or as potent as the belch of a volcano.

Some flyers no doubt regard clouds as little better than a menace, something to be avoided, the complexion of evil weather which they must combat and conquer. Yet to the more sensitive, even the blandest of clouds can be symbolic of great unseen forces which winged man is just now beginning to comprehend. Obviously all clouds mean something, and even though their Rosetta stone may be undiscovered we can already sense that they tell of the contours and temperatures of continents and seas—letting some of the form of the earth show through.

By the close of the nineteenth century, clouds had been pretty well catalogued and classified—both by shape and behavior, and their hidden natures were beginning to be understood. The basic types were four: the *cirrus* which comes from the Latin word for "curl" because these clouds often look like wisps of curly hair as they float in the upper sky; the *stratus* type from the Latin for "spread out" because they

are like great soft blankets spread out across the light of day; the *nimbus* from the Latin "rain," being the spongy, wet, low-scudding kind of clouds that characteristically douse us with their rainy contents; and the *cumulus* meaning "heap" in Latin, which are the common fair-weather clouds that heap themselves upward into beautiful mountainlike shapes, sometimes turning into tremendous thunderheads that fill the sky.

Of course there are innumerable variations and combinations of these clouds and a few special extra ones which make up the unlimited panoply of the actual skyscape, but these four types remain the foundations of cloud classification today.

The cirrus are the highest of the regular workaday clouds, which seems to give them something of a special ethereal nature. They are the wing feathers of the wind and have been seen from two hundred miles away. They have neither the thunderous voice of the cumulus nor the wet cargo of nimbus, but silently flick their horse tails and their dainty plumes like a kind of elite fairy cavalry that no ordinary earthlings can hope to approach. Because of their height they seem to move slowly even though their real speed is commonly more than a hundred miles an hour. They are calm in aspect and very cool. In actuality they are the birthplace of snow—fine powdery snow that floats six miles up in summer and winter alike, seldom relaxing its steadfast grip on the sky to let a handful of Heaven's purity flutter its way to earth.

The actual material of the cirrus is tenuous indeed: ice crystals spread out about 5000 to the cubic foot, which is only 3 per cubic inch and much less dense than the substance of ordinary clouds. Cirrus wisps and tufts sometimes become almost invisible when you fly close to them, revealing a kind of unearthly, optic shyness like that of the rainbow.

Yet they are completely real and they perform a strange but natural drama that meteorology has hardly begun to understand. At medium range many look more like frozen cascades than strands of hair, and this is exactly what they turn out to be. A German cloud pioneer called them *Fallstreifen,* or "fall streaks" having discovered that, when visible, this type of cirrus is actually composed of slowly falling ice trails. It is similar in dynamic principle to spindrift on the sea, the streaks of spume blown off the crests of breaking waves.

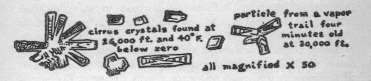

cirrus crystals found at 26,000 ft. and 40° F. below zero

particle from a vapor trail four minutes old at 30,000 ft.

all magnified X 50

As the sky's wind almost always decreases in speed with a decrease in height, the crystals that fall soon get left behind the cloud they fell from. Evaporating and shrinking as they descend, they drift behind in visible curved streaks like handfuls of fine seed sown by angels upon a fallow sky, there left on the wind to blossom into some future life still hidden from our little view.

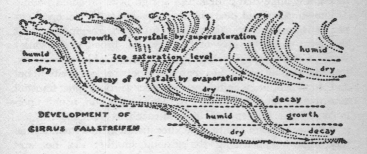

growth of crystals by supersaturation
humid
ice saturation level
humid
dry
dry
decay of crystals by evaporation
dry
decay
DEVELOPMENT OF
humid
growth
CIRRUS FALLSTREIFEN
dry
decay

The fluffy tops of some cirrus forms are made of water droplets as well as tiny snow, but these are not truly cirrus yet and they seldom last long, for their snow is growing as their water dries and they too soon fall transformed into the graceful fibrous curves that are their priceless contribution to beauty in the sky.

Other examples of cirrus are born of the slipstreams of

passing airplanes, sired by exhaust fumes, mothered in the womb of wind, slowly growing from vapor trails into great shimmering stripes, half a mile wide, perhaps eventually descending into the largo ripples of mackerel scales. And sometimes you see natural cirrus arranged uncannily into endless radiating bands that cover the sky like the meridians of the celestial globe from horizon to horizon in straight lines which, like railroad tracks, appear to meet at one point in the distance.

When cirrus clouds begin to thicken and compromise with lower clouds, naturally they are given different names. First after cirrus in the usual sequence comes the gauzelike stratified form known as cirro-stratus, the milk cloud, a high milky cobweb veil made of ice crystals that barely dims the sun and moon yet creates halos around both, sometimes rainbow halos when the film is curdling still further into cirro-cumulus, the mackerel sky.

As the milk cloud is flattening and descending toward stratus, it normally soon warms up, its crystals melt into droplets, and it develops into the low dense blanket of that name, a change that is definitely a sign of approaching rain.

The stratus cloud bears no resemblance to the ethereal cirrus. It is by contrast earthy, homespun, often shapeless. It is the great-plains country of the sky, the broad aerial valley floor. It is the conservative member, the stable personality, the wet blanket of the heavens that poets seldom write about and few people definitely remember. It does not transmit sunshine nor does it completely blot out the sun, usually permitting just a dim spot of light to reach its underside.

It tends to seem the drabber because it is undynamic: neither high nor brushing the ground, neither dry nor wet enough for an exciting shower. It is a kind of Tory fog of the lower levels (about two thousand feet up). It is the Scottish mist, its brightest color a dour bluish gray, its strongest rain a slow steady drizzle.

But the circumstance of perhaps greatest significance in the stratus is the fact that it represents a temperature inversion—or nearly so. That means that the stratus is born when the normal condition of warmer air near the ground and cooler higher up is reversed or reduced. It is exactly the opposite of the cumulus which appears when that condition is accentuated, when hot air below bursts through the cold, condensing into visible vertical form. The stratus by contrast is an utterly horizontal cloud and kept so by complete absence of vertical currents. It is the epitome of equilibrium, the stolid envoy of peace.

Sometimes the stratus cousin called alto-stratus at around 10,000 feet becomes so thin it is semi-transparent like the surface of a calm sea—silent and still as you fly over it, yet arranged in slight waves like a sheet of gauze lying on the beach. Through this veil you can look down on the colorful anatomy of the landscape, green and yellow fields and glistening ribbons of roads and white streams and purple hills crouching, appearing through the thin cloud like the gaudy bottom of a tropic lagoon.

At other times this same cloud becomes fibrous like a great cobweb and floats in beautiful silky whorls or, having thickened, may look from above like nothing in the world but a field of snow as you skim above it in your winged toboggan—league upon league of it—a kind of subjective arctic plain, a glacier of the mind.

From below, alto-stratus is often dark enough to blot out the sun's outline completely though sometimes it seems illumined from inside like a frosted bulb. It is the same thing as ground fog raised a few thousand feet into the air and drifting along on the breeze in tattered spongy blotches.

When the stratus or alto-stratus evolves into a real rain cloud it is called the nimbo-stratus. Then it becomes heavy and low and ragged, sometimes mixed with soggy cumulus, and it emits a steady pattering rain.

In modern meteorology there is no longer any such cloud as the pure nimbus of old, it being recognized that this ancient drencher is really the rain-producing development of two of the other main kinds of cloud: stratus and cumulus. The nimbo-stratus, already described, is the rainy aspect of the low-strung well-tempered stratus breed. It forms a ceiling at 3000 feet on the average, though often much lower, and has been found to produce rain or snow within four hours in seventy-three per cent of all cases, this precipitation averaging eight hours' duration in winter, but varying widely in individual cases.

The cumulo-nimbus on the other hand is the big rainy brother of the rough, radical cumulus cloud and he heaves into being as the cumulus grows into a thunderhead and starts tossing his weight around to his favorite accompaniment of thunder and lightning. Cumulo-nimbus is probably the most violent and dangerous of all clouds, and we will come to its details presently. The straight nimbus aspect, indistinct as it is, might be summed up as the soggy, scudding bottom parts of clouds that come stampeding low over the hills like rampant mustangs, tossing their soft manes about them, their bodies passing darkly before the east wind and kicking out behind not dust but drenching rain.

The cumulus, the last of the basic clouds, is the most dynamic of all. It is the head end of a wind that blows straight up. It is the vertical cloud which grows high as much as wide or handsome. It is the healthy, heaping helping of normal fair weather. It is the white woolly sheep cloud that looks like a puff of steam cut off square at the bottom.

That, in fact, is just about what a cumulus cloud is: a puff of steam or hot humid air. And it is cut off square at the bottom by the horizontal condensation level below which the air is warm enough to hold its moisture unseen. So to visualize a cumulus cloud correctly you need to see it as only the visible capital of a tall transparent column of hot air. Or perhaps it would be more exact to describe the column as shaped like a tree, for it is strong and steady and narrow near the base, spreading and branching and tossing about in the breeze as it goes upward. It is by nature almost exactly like the rising column of smoke over a campfire, but so much bigger than it seems to be standing still and, being mostly clear air instead of smoke, its main body is invisible.

One reason so little of the heat tree can normally be seen is that the upward flow of warm air has a kind of anchor that usually stops its rise shortly after it condenses into visible form, thus strictly limiting the cloud. This anchor is the cooling and weighting down of the cloud as it expands in the thin upper air. Expansion has a cooling effect on any gas —you have noticed the coldness of the air hissing out of a deflating tire—and when the cloud gets as cool as the surrounding air it is not light and buoyant enough to rise any higher.

That is the way it usually happens—on a normal sunny day. And it is just as well, else the sky would be one great perpetual thunderstorm and life on earth would be far wetter and noiser and more dangerous than it is already.

Cumulus clouds usually appear around ten o'clock on a sunny morning as the ground heats up and starts those columns of hot air bubbling upwards. Quite suddenly you notice them springing to eye all over the sky and all at the same altitude, perhaps three or four thousand feet up. From then on they grow slowly larger until late afternoon when their sources of heat are cut off.

Along a coastline you can often see these cumulus sheep grazing high over the sunbaked land while over the cooler sea the sky remains an empty blue because updrafts of air are too feeble there to give clouds birth. This observable fact, by the way, was very important to the ancient South Sea navigators, for even a small sunny atoll will usually puff up enough heat to produce a lone fleecy cloud which may float all day a mile above it like a cosmic lighthouse, pointing the way to land from ten times as far out at sea as the island itself can be seen. What better could a Micronesian helmsman wish to steer by?

Something every glider pilot needs do is study these cumulus forms, and especially the unseen heat streams that create them. They are his propellor, his spark, his gasoline. Except perhaps for windward hillsides they are his main staircase to altitude. He knows them as thermals or "cloud streets" and one of his favorite tactics is gliding from one to another of these unseen elevators across the country, spiraling upward in each to gain what height he lost between.

Nowadays the glider pilot already has a wealth of experience behind him. He knows all the signs. He has delicate instruments for reading temperature and altitude too. Sometimes he even outsoars the birds, as recently happened to one of the crack glider men of Southern California. This pilot was soaring across the desert, thermal by thermal, minding his own business when he picked himself such a powerful updraft that he began spiraling skyward so fast he attracted the attention of an eagle, a hawk, and three buzzards which joined in behind him, evidently doing their best to follow his example. And the rising wind even picked up pieces of dead sagebrush and tumbleweed and carried this and other debris swirling aloft among the birds and around the plane—up and up for nineteen thousand feet, ending inside and near the top of a large cumulus thunderhead! When he finally emerged none of the birds were to be seen anywhere.

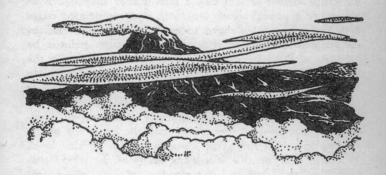

Most ordinary clouds, as you've noticed if you have ever lain on your back in the grass, drift slowly along on the wind, eventually disappearing below the horizon. But they have some strange cousins that behave very differently, defying the winds as if literally tied to the earth. You see these generally near mountain peaks and they are in fact tied to the earth by invisible thongs of humid air that spring from solid ground, that may reach up from any orographic configuration bold enough to deflect moist currents up into the cold.

The best known of fixed clouds is probably the banner cloud which streams like a flag from a high peak—continuously gaining new substance as valley air, riding up a mountainside on the wind's back, condenses near the crest—continuously evaporating old substance at its tattered flagtail end perhaps a mile to leeward as the air mixes with drier air or subsides to a warmer level. Thus the wind blows right through the banner cloud instead of carrying it along—just as if it were a flag of cloth.

Another stand-still cloud familiar to mountaineers is the crest or cap cloud, a kind of tablecloth of fog that drapes itself snugly upon summits. Like the banner cloud it lets the wind blow through it, eating condensation on the one side, voiding evaporation on the other. It is also called the helm cloud or foehn wall through which the foehn winds blow.

The third stay-put cloud is the strangest and loveliest of all, the lenticular or lens cloud. It is usually shaped like an almond or a surreal convex lens with tapering pointed edges and, like a lens, often shows iridescent colors around its circumference. It looks as if it might have been painted by Dali. As with the last two clouds, it remains stationary in the windy sky, balancing condensation with evaporation, often miles from a hill so that its air leash from earth is hard to trace. Yet it is anchored securely by a standing wave of air that billows up from some irregularity of ground to windward. It may be high enough to mark the beginning of the stratosphere or it may float close to the low stratus level. Wherever it is found it is a living graph of the wind's true path, the fixed white cap of a standing billow of air—as real as a stopped clock, as graceful as the flying tresses of Aura—cool, beautiful, unearthly.

More mysterious but of a similar ilk are the shy nacreous or mother-of-pearl clouds that stand still at an altitude of from fourteen to twenty miles: three times the height of cirrus. These rare clouds that are seldom seen except in polar regions when a foehn wind is blowing at ground level are now known to be lenticular in nature and normally composed of ice crystals which by refraction create the pearly iridescence observed. They are perhaps best known to Norwegian weather men in Oslo who see them in the clear evening skies as the dry west wind descends from the mountains in the wake of a storm. They show up at night almost as plainly as by day, sometimes remaining luminous three hours after sunset.

I know of only one kind of earth cloud loftier and rarer than the nacreous, and that is the very aloof one called noctilucent. Measured at more than fifty miles above the ground and illumined by the sun virtually all night, it is believed to be composed of very fine, dry volcanic dust, or perhaps the faint, powdery ash of meteors. It is seen in the north only from the latitude of Canada and northern Europe, myster-

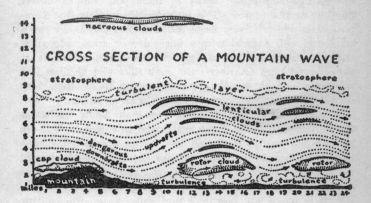

iously lingering close to the horizon, seldom observed as high as 10°. Few noctilucent clouds have been reported since World War I, although they were frequently seen on summer nights for a few years after the 1883 explosion of Krakatoa, the Siberian meteor of 1908, and the lesser blowup of Katmai in 1912. They are silvery white at the top, yellowish gold nearer the bottom, rarely faintly bluish but never iridescent. And sometimes among them at the same low angle lurk darker clouds which, curiously enough, are not lucent at all.

The opposite extreme from noctilucent in the cloud hierarchy is the ground cloud, fog, which is actually nothing more than an ordinary stratus resting on the earth. When you encounter it while driving along a mountain road you could as well call it cloud as fog. Then would be a good time to take careful note of the cloud's intimate texture at first hand, its living flesh. Some clouds are juicier than others, some of coarser grain. There is just as much variation in cloud substance as in that of meats, cloths, or stones.

Most stratus clouds, especially of the nimbus affiliation, are spongy and rather fleshy of body with porous tatters hanging at the bottom. The microscopic droplets that compose them are relatively large. But cumulus clouds are more solid and well defined with a finer, denser grain, becoming cottony and fibrous as they get drier and cooler usually at their frayed tops. Cirrus are the most silky and fibrillated of all, but you could hardly get near enough to see their very delicate diamond dust texture except in an airplane.

Fog is generally divided into two main kinds: radiation fog and advection fog. They are similar in substance but are created differently. Radiation fog is the stay-at-home type that forms usually on clear summer nights when the humid air loses heat by radiating it into the sky, resulting in condensation as it becomes too cool to hold its moisture invisibly. It is rarely 500 feet thick and clears soon after sunrise. Its droplets are orderly and uniform in size.

Advection fog, however, is the traveling type such as often rolls in from the sea, sometimes a mile thick, its droplets assorted, having formed when the moist salt air condensed under varying conditions in passing over relatively cool parts of the sea or land.

Radiation fog is a kind of dew of the whole air for, just as dew is air moisture condensed on cooling objects like grass and trees, fog is air moisture condensed throughout cooling air as a whole. It saturates the surfaces of trees, houses, or anything the air touches, leaving what is known as fog drip, which is not dew but a kind of fog gravy as different from dew as tears are from sweat.

Advection fog is formed horizontally almost exactly as cumulus clouds are formed vertically. It is what pours through the Golden Gate upon San Francisco on humid afternoons, or creeps in from the Grand Banks and down the coast of Nova Scotia. It condenses as it cools by advection, by motion over cool surfaces. It may last for days.

Fog is not at all the same thing as haze, which is formed of dust rather than mere moisture and has a bluish tinge. But in these days of rapidly multiplying factories when so much smoke is spewed upforth, fog is commonly combined with various amounts of haze and smoke—even unto the sulphurous smog of the industrial metropolis, or the blinding four-foot visibility of the "London perticular." Formerly almost pure white, fog today is often streaked with gray, sometimes with an overlayer close to black.

The most deadly smog of the past century was undoubtedly the one that hit London early in December 1952, and is now credited with 4000 deaths and millions of dollars worth of property destroyed. It started as a white fog on Thursday, December 4, turned dark gray by the week end, and ended almost black from the soft-coal smoke of a million fires. While the warm layer above the city called an "inversion roof" kept the fog droplets from rising and dispersing, the microscopic flakes of soot kept the numbers of smoke particles per cubic centimeter extremely high and the interjacent air abnormally dry. By the third day, old people with asthma or bronchitis began to get frightened, and oxygen tents were in great demand. Blondes were turning into brunettes. An airplane that managed to make an instrument landing at Croydon got lost between the runway and the ramp. Blind men were helping as street guides in the city, firemen groped in front of their engines, while dock police were busy trying to rescue those who had walked off wharves into the Thames and could be heard calling and blubbering hopelessly somewhere in the filmy water. People in theaters could not see the stage from the sixth row and projected moving pictures could not penetrate to the screens. Sounds of choking could be heard everywhere, mingled with distant church bells and the muffled clanging of ambulances. The whole city seemed to be suspended in the sky, floating in a cloud—cool, dank, inviolate.

I am in a different world of course when I fly over such a weather clot in an airplane, and it is hard to remember how it can feel to be submerged in the sea of particles below; the whole thing looks so different from outside. Streaky, sooty fogs from the sky can be as beautiful as the purest marble. They are slow-moving seas or fast-flowing glaciers—rivers of vapor that reveal the wimpling and snurling of air as plainly as brooks show the rippling of water—by day their whorls gray and brown, sometimes with interfolds of yellow, lavender, or red—by night the lights of cities pulsing dimly through this glowing flesh of the weary brow of earth.

A noted psychologist said, "There is nothing in imagina-

tion that was not previously in sense." The clouds of the world are ever trying to prove him right, dramatizing before our innocence all the art of the millenniums, bestowing upon us the shape of the divine manifestation that we may have material for our learning.

They are of subtle material, the clouds—don't mistake.

They are not to be appreciated except from the remotest perspective in space and thought. Beside them the trafficking of our little orb may appear quite mad when any of us becomes detached enough to see it.

7

Thunder, Hail, and Rain

ERNIE SILVERS lay asleep in the top bunk, snoring gently, with his head phones on and connected by an extension wire to his radio. I had just been trying to get a bearing on the same set but had put the phones aside in disgust. All I could hear was the wail of a discordant sky, the sizzle of electron collisions in continuous ionic frustration.

Yet this harsh sound was as peaceful as the kettle on the stove to Ernie. He slept on and on—until suddenly there came into his subconsciousness a faint pattern of meaning: ". . . whooewmeeee —dah — di — dah — dimoueeeei — didi — di — dit — deeommm — di — di — dah — aaehooumm — dah — dit — mmmmmmeeeoo — dah — di — dah — dit — eeooo — di — di-di-dit — 000000 — di — di — dah — 0000emmm . . ."

Ernie opened his eyes instantly. C—H—U—N, he thought. Those were our own call letters. In ten seconds he was at his desk responding to the call, which came from another plane half an hour behind us. It was a routine check, but to me seemed a significant demonstration of human adaptability to radio waves—response of the human mind to something a hundred miles away in the sky—if not beyond the horizon at least hidden behind an ocean flowing with quadrillions of molecules. It was a tuning in on part of the great mystery of the total electric forces of nature—forces that have scarcely begun to be resolved even in the limited pragmatic understandings of industry.

It made me think of the time the big flash came a few years ago when we were flying out of Miami to Puerto Rico. It was my first personal acquaintance with a stroke of lightning. Had I not been in an airplane—one of the safest places to be when lightning comes your way—it might also have been my last.

We were in a C–87 and had just ridden through three minutes of the most violent turbulence I think I ever experienced. As I was beginning to wonder how much longer our wing spars could stand the terrific bouncing—up—down—up—slantwise—skewways—down—up—up—down, suddenly it happened! The cockpit lit up like a neon tube. It lasted less than a thousandth of a second, yet huge pale green sparks jumped all over the room, including one to the pilot's pedestal. The radio man was knocked to the floor and the hairs on the back of my head stood as stiff as bristles.

The lightning bolt had evidently struck our trailing antenna and followed it to the tail of the airplane—then on into the radio itself, which was severely damaged. From the radio it had branched out into the skin of the airplane by way of several score of little aluminum rivets, most of which were blasted completely out of the ship, leaving empty holes.

What is the strange power behind such a bolt out of the seeming unsubstantial sky—such a ruthless stabbing of the darkling air? Is it something in the dynamic of the particular cloud?

The thunderstorm comes to our attention as the culminating drama of all clouds. More precisely is thunder the natural temper of the great cumulo-nimbus, the free expression of runaway heat turned explosive.

Men have long made obeisance to Thor, the thunder god. They have not understood him, even those who visited him in his ancient home of Buitenzorg in Java where thunder has been heard during 322 of the 365 days of the year, more than anywhere else on earth. But they have recognized him as a major god. They have trembled even to see his "messengers," those small cumulus clouds that precede him in the sky for they remember well the mighty wrath that follows.

The natural causes of the thunderstorm were probably not systematically investigated until Benjamin Franklin tried to catch a few particles of lightning through his kite string in 1752, which led to his invention of the lightning rod. And it was Franklin also who suspected and proved that storms do not just grow and rage in one locality but move progressively across continents and seas.

No one, even among the ancients, had doubted that great violence occurred in the fully aroused cumulo-nimbus, yet actually measuring the muscle of this monster was another thing again. It remained for the latter days of the airplane for man to penetrate the beating heart of the thundercloud to see what makes it roar.

In the nineteen twenties and thirties with this in mind, many daring pilots, even glidermen, flew and soared straight into thunderclouds and quite a few lived to tell about it—though often with more emotion than objectivity.

Usually their tales went something like this: "I don't know where I went, but it was terrific. I seemed to be thrown up, then down so violently and so often I thought my wings would come off. The rain beat on me in sheets, and the lightning scared me silly! All I could think of was: Am I going to get out of this alive?"

And too often they didn't get out alive. At a glider meeting in the Rhön Mountains just before World War II five Hitler-inspired pilots soared into a huge thunderhead and were whirled upward with horrifying violence. All of them soon jumped for their lives, opening their parachutes as they fell blindly through the turbulent air for fear they might be dashed upon a mountain. But it was a deadly mistake. The mighty updraft filled the parachutes almost to bursting and whooshed the men up like feathers, pelting them with sharp hail as they got into the freezing levels. And they kept on going up till they froze stiff at what must have been at least 30,000 feet and thirty below zero. They became literally human hailstones and may have been blown up and down for a long time before the wrathful Thor was through with them. Only one landed alive and he lost three fingers and most of his face before he got out of the hospital.

It was the development of radar during World War II, making it possible for the first time to keep exact track of an airplane or a balloon in the thickest cloud or wildest rain, that finally solved the mystery of the thunderstorm. The job was started just after the war by the large-scale Thunderstorm Project organized for the United States government by Horace R. Byers, a crack weather man at the University of Chicago, with planes and equipment of the Air Force, Navy and U.S. Weather Bureau co-operating.

And after about a year of dangerous and intensive work, followed by three years of exhaustive calculation, the thunderstorm was at last revealed to have quite a complex nature, in fact in some ways a kind of animal nature since it turned out to be composed of cells that grow and fuse and multiply.

The storm begins, modestly enough, with a single cumulus cloud which develops what Byers named the "mother cell." This cell is at first just a very strong updraft of warm air which rises so fast it penetrates the ceiling that halts ordinary cumulus clouds. That is, instead of cooling itself by expansion as it goes up until it is as cool as the surrounding air, this ferocious updraft rises so fast it gets into cold air faster than it can cool itself. Furthermore its condensation into cloud is so rapid that it actually generates a lot of heat. Just as you feel cold when water is evaporating from your skin and would be warmed by the opposite (condensation) so is the thundercloud. Therefore a kind of chain reaction excites the rising cloud, producing more and more heat relative to surrounding air as the cloud builds up. It is actually a kind of explosion of course. In this connection it is interesting to realize that the dramatic mushroom bomb cloud is just an artificial form of cumulus which, like any thunderhead, may eventually start to fray into cirrus fibers after the frigid heights have flattened its top.

By the time the mother cell has attained a diameter of four miles or so, its updraft may be boiling skyward at 160 m.p.h. or more, whirling increasingly outward until its anvil crest is half a dozen miles long as well as eight or ten miles high. Its main body may also contain an incipient tornado, though this in most cases will be a matter of definition, to say nothing of being factually unverifiable. At any rate the cell is now (after ten minutes of rapid growth) changing from what is called the cumulus stage into the mature stage. Its rising droplets of condensing moisture, having passed the freezing level, begin to coalesce with the ice crystals, forming rain or hail. And when the raindrops or hailstones have grown too big to be held up by the updraft they start to fall —first in the weaker parts of the rising cloud, then spreading to the whole cell—a change of direction at just the height that effectively forms the flat top of the characteristic anvil, which is then tapered by the wind to a leeward point.

This downward motion of cool precipitation naturally drags along a good deal of air with it, creating by air friction a cold downdraft right in the middle of the hot updraft—specifically in the center of what corresponds to the eye of the thunder cell. The ensuing wild battle of vertical winds, hot and cold, is the secret of the well-known turbulence of the thundercloud: violent upwinds and downwinds so close together that they can flip an airplane upside down in a second or break its wings in one mighty pneumatic bounce.

Even when such an ordeal fails to throw an airplane out of control it has been known to kill or injure persons aboard, not to mention wrecking valuable equipment. I will never forget having part of the floor of a C–54 explode in turbulent air one day near the end of World War II when our hydraulic system blew apart over the Atlantic—leaving us the ticklish problem of landing twenty-two seriously wounded soldiers in Newfoundland without benefit of flaps, landing gear, or brakes.

The cold downdrafts in thunderstorms were not formerly much known as compared to the more obvious updrafts, but it is the cold downdrafts that do most of the damage on the earth. They also eventually win the battle of up against down with the help of their artillery of hail, snow pellets or rain, steadily increasing in size and strength, squeezing the updrafts, growing more violent as they descend to the ground with their thundering downpour. Then whooshing outward along the earth beyond the rain, these winds often reach 60 or 70 m.p.h., their cold-air mass shaped something like a foot, the toes reaching out several miles ahead of the storm, the heel following close behind.

It is where these cold foot gusts kicking outward from the mother cell meet other winds that new updrafts are started, which grow into new cells—young cumulus children of the mother cell who is passing her prime. The baby cells thus bud forth all around their tiring mother, springing upward in new heat explosions, some so close they fuse with mother or each other, some several miles away. Their cumulus forms shoot up into the freezing levels again, causing fresh condensation into rain and hail—fresh outbursts of lightning and thunder—fresh feet of cold wind.

Here is as good a place as any to point out, in verification of coriolis effect, that as northern thunderstorms approach their maturity the inblowing winds that feed their updrafts turn slowly *counterclockwise* around the *low* pressure vortex, while in the later stages of the same storms the downdrafts that nourish the outblowing winds turn *clockwise* around the newly created *high* pressure region at the ground. Thus at intermediate stages in most thunderstorms there must normally be two vortexes, one inside the other, simultaneously spiraling (sometimes very slowly) in opposite directions!

Meanwhile as the descending central downpour of rain increases, dragging more and more air with it, the mature stage of the cell (after half an hour) has passed into the dissipating stage which presently culminates in the total cessation of updraft. All that remains of violence now is falling downward to earth, slowly and more slowly. Thus the great thermodynamic engine eventually exhausts itself and the earth beneath is cooled and the barometer rises back toward equilibrium.

This evolutionary process meanwhile is being repeated in the offspring thunder cells and cloud towers which keep springing up like amoebas, generation by generation, each turret rising higher than the last, rolling and slowly subsiding, different cells in different stages of life at any one time —the great cells, pouring over the earth together like the plague—the whole "thunderstorm complex" leapfrogging forward cell by cell across the world.

These complex sequences of thermodynamic and coriolis

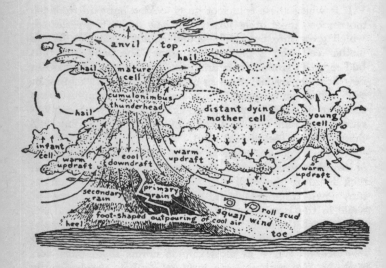

cause and effect (which have their varying parallels in hurricanes, tornadoes, and the circumpolar jet streams) explain in a general way the cloud development and the wind and rain of a thunderstorm. But what of the thunder and lightning that are the distinguishing features of this familiar yet mysterious storm? What is the electrodynamic basis for the flashing fury around us?

So much research is now going on in this field, with inconclusive and contradictory indications, that it is hard to generalize without risking serious errors—but at least some of the principal facts are becoming clearer and a consensus of scientific opinion is forming.

The sudden upthrust of warm, moist lower air into the shocking cold of the frozen heights is the creative basis for thunder. It is also the prime earthly example of static electricity generated by friction. The furious friction of the clash develops static electricity on a gigantic scale and the electrical potential in turn triggers the lightning and thunder. Thus the flashing might of the thunderstorm is an almost direct consequence of millions of warm water droplets being hurled into comparable masses of brittle ice crystals—colliding with them, rolling over them, here melting them, there being frozen by them into combined pellets of snow, into seeds of potential hail.

The exact proportions of electric charge developed by the many and complex dynamic forces of this battle of heat and cold are still a matter of conjecture. Some investigators think the action of wind against the rain is the principal factor, that it tears off the outer surface of each falling drop like pulling a sweater over a child's head, making a fine negatively charged mist while leaving the main part of the drop positive. Some think that electricity is born to the sky by the bursting of tiny air bubbles in the melting snow or hail. Some hold that the friction of snow crystals splintering in the wind sets up the static charge. Others think that freezing somehow generates potentials in the infant ice, or that it may be the tiny eddies in the slip streams around the falling snow. In reality it may well be all these factors and more that combine to do the work.

In any case huge masses of charged rain droplets and hail and baby snow become sorted into preponderantly positive and negative reservoirs of electrical energy at different parts of the thunderhead, creating between them fields of very great extremes in potential. It is the discharge of energy through such fields upon the sudden breakdown of intervening resistance that we call lightning.

There are nearly similar electrical fields of course extending between clouds and from the clouds to the earth. Normally the positive pole is located high in a cloud, the negative on earth, but sometimes this is reversed; and two parts of the ground adjoining each other may be oppositely charged.

The mechanism of the actual strike of lightning that sooner or later discharges the differences in potential in the sky is one of the most intricate of meteorological phenomena. It begins with the pressing of an atomic "button" by a single electron, which triggers what physicists call a "streamer mechanism," which in turn clears a path and sets off the "cataclysmic burst of electrons" that is the main charge.

One such stroke of lightning however often does not drain a cloud of enough of its potential, which may immediately recharge from other sources, so that there can be repeated strokes in rapid succession down a single channel. A high-speed camera has actually recorded forty consecutive strokes within the time span of a second—effectively demolishing the legend that "lightning never strikes twice in the same place."

The evidence is that there are slow rhythms of lightning frequency also, each thunderstorm cell having peaks of intensity about every eighteen minutes, which is the average interval between the rise of turrets. As each thunderhead turret thrusts its top upward in turn, rising at about 12 m.p.h. then receding at 8 m.p.h., the whole cloud rotating ponderously, the electrical fields naturally follow suit, successive lightning strokes now tapping higher and higher regions of cloud, now lower and lower, playing up and down the scales of potentiality like the bagpiper of spring.

If such behavior seems a little fantastic it is really just

what science has discovered about the thunderstorm and its fearful lightning that so long defied all man's efforts to understand it. For now its stroke has been measured in length all the way from five hundred feet to nine miles! In thickness, from the equal of a fine wire to more than a foot when it fades from visibility. Its thunder at close range is the explosive crack of shock waves sent out by the lightning channel's few micro-seconds of expansion, waves that have been seen to make a rainbow literally quiver in the sky like a plucked harp string. In the distance its rumble is a blending of reports from sundry segments, repeated strokes, and echoes near and far. Beyond eighteen miles, though it cannot be heard, its reflected flicker of light from over the horizon is seen as "heat lightning," its flash diffused in dense cloud as "sheet lightning."

Some of the sky's lightnings are actually too "slow" to produce thunder, taking as much as a tenth of a second to expand to size—which is even slower than quick human hands can move. Some lightning helps farmers by fertilizing their soil, combining chemically with rain into a world-wide "100 million tons of valuable nitrogen fertilizer every year."

The most powerful single stroke of lightning ever recorded in the United States pointedly hit the University of Pittsburgh's "Cathedral of Learning" on July 31, 1947, charging it with 345,000 amperes or enough current to light 600,000 sixty-watt bulbs for the duration of the flash: 35/1,000,000 of a second.

Very different from such a well-grounded building, however, is an airplane flying high above the earth. If it should become in any way grounded in flight an airplane would suffer greatly from lightning. But I do not know of any case of lightning directly causing an airplane accident. Ninety per cent of the few lightning hits on commercial aircraft, according to the records, have happened at night in maximum turbulence when it was raining or snowing and within 6° F. of the freezing point. These incidents almost always occur between 12,000 and 20,000 feet, where vertical winds are at their strongest, and are generally preceded by St. Elmo's fire.

Saint Elmo, if you will remember, was the beloved Bishop

of Formiae in ancient Italy 1650 years ago, whom Mediterranean sailors have ever since been invoking for aid during storms. It was natural to name the corposant after him—that visible discharge of static electricity that is commonly seen "on the tops of the masts and the tips of the spars" at sea before thunderstorms, and in our day playing about the wing tips and propellers of airplanes in soft bluish tongues of light. That this eerie corona is a real omen of lightning is statistically accepted beyond question, and it is now believed to be formed by the glowing passage of billions of electrons quietly discharging their local differences amid the field sources of lightning. It is also known that it can be dangerous in itself for it has been explicitly convicted of causing the explosion of the airship *Hindenburg* at Lakehurst, N.J., in 1937 by igniting a mixture of valved hydrogen and air as the famous dirigible came in after a successful crossing from Germany.

Probably closely related to St. Elmo's fire is the strange ball lightning that so long has baffled science. I have only seen it once, bouncing slowly along the ground in a thunderstorm downpour, but there are innumerable records of its astonishing doings. I once read a French account of a "fire ball" that in October 1898 appeared in a room in Marseilles and advanced toward a small girl sitting on a table with her legs dangling. Rising as it came close, the fiery sphere, surrounded by a glowing haze, circled the terrified child twice before darting up the chimney to explode on the roof with "an appalling crash that shook the whole house."

Years later a similar "ball of fire" was seen to hit the ground in an English village, breaking into two parts, both of which bounded to a nearby roof to enter separate chimneys—evidently a favored route. One part descended into a cellar and exploded, wrecking a valuable chicken brooder, while the other in a different house glided quietly through a room in which a man was reading to a boy. Leaving them both untouched, it burned a small hole in the floor and plunged into a sheepfold below. Several young lambs jumping about were not hurt, but five large sheep were killed one by one. The shepherd's son standing in an open doorway was then astonished to see the glowing object squeeze past him out into a yard and off across a field almost as if it had a mind of its own.

An explanation for this kind of stalled thunderbolt is that it is really not lightning at all but "a creeping corona discharge" that advances along "a relatively intense portion of the electric field." The electric field itself is evidently full of unaccountable wrinkles and irregularities.

Cattle and sheep seem to be particularly vulnerable to most varieties of lightning and there is a recorded case on a Utah mountainside of one bolt killing 835 sheep, evidently because the dry earth offered more resistance than the roundabout route of traveling "from the ground, up one leg, through the moist body, and down another leg . . ."

Of all known kinds of lightning I think the rarest must be the literal "bolt from the blue" or thunderbolt out of a cloudless sky. Like the invisible tornado it has occasionally been known to happen, but your chances of being blitzed by a clear sky are virtually nil. Even your much more likely chances of ultimately being done to death by a thunderstorm in the United States are statistically no greater than one in 365,000 (assuming you are as foolish as the average person), which is only 1/35 as likely as being killed by one of the much rarer but deadlier tornadoes.

You might think the former a negligible risk and one you couldn't do much about anyway, but it is really quite possible to improve your prospects significantly. During one five-year period last century, records show that the British Navy lost seventy ships to lightning, mostly by having masts struck at sea, the bolt traveling all the way down to the step, then blasting a hole through the bottom. But today's ships, like modern power lines, airplanes, and many a house, are protected and seldom get hurt by lightning.

Even a man whose work exposes him almost daily to lightning can do something about it for, despite the saying that you will never know it if lightning strikes you, one can sometimes feel the bolt coming and if quick enough take evasive action in time. A lineman I know of in Indiana can testify to this, for he was working on a powerline pole one afternoon in a thunderstorm and suddenly realized his hair was standing on end and that a great magnetic tension was building up in the air all around the pole. Realizing what it meant, he quickly unbuckled his safety belt and threw himself full length upon the nearest cross-arm. Just then the lightning struck the pole and, vaporizing 130 feet of heavy wire, leaped to another pole, and from there to the ground. The lineman was knocked unconscious, but his prompt action had saved his life.

I was surprised when I first learned that hail is much more dangerous than lightning in the sky. This is only too true however, for hail not only needs no grounding to take effect but it can float in treacherous ambush in apparently empty air while awaiting opportunity to dive-bomb its unsuspecting victim at almost any height.

A few years ago an American Airlines plane suffered more than ten thousand dollars worth of damage while flying in clear air within half a mile of a large thundercloud. The pilot had not thought the great white anvil soaring innocently high above his wing tip could endanger him so long as he kept clear of the actual cloud, but the beautiful canopy and its scarflike fringe had already dispatched a barrage of invisible heavy hail which struck him out of the blue like a volley of golf balls, denting the wings and fuselage so seriously that half the duralumin skin of the airplane had to be replaced.

Hail is born in cumuliform clouds, particularly in thunderclouds. It is the stepson of violence, growing in distinct cycles or steps. It begins when raindrops get caught in such a wild updraft that they are swept up to freezing levels and turned to ice. If they fall to earth right after this they usually melt on the way down, becoming rain again—or if the air is cold enough may land as small hail.

But if they are to be larger they must go through many steps of this kind of growth before they reach earth as hail—many ups and downs in the turbulent engine of thunder.

This has been shown by the numerous coats of different kinds of ice found in large hailstones. Each time they fall through the rain cloud they take on a wet coat. Each time they are whisked upward again this wetness freezes into a new coat of ice, which may be clear ice or rime ice depending on the rate of freezing. Clear ice is quick-frozen like the ice cubes in your freezer compartment. But grainy rime ice accumulates slowly like the refrigerator's coat of frost that needs defrosting. It commonly grows in the sky from cloud droplets (not rain) coating a hailstone while it is falling through a supercooled cloud, a cloud that is unfrozen but below freezing temperature—an unstable condition common in clouds above the freezing level and which requires only the passage of a solid object like an airplane to produce ice. Almost any sequence of ice textures may thus clothe the hail, and the longer the vertical wind circulation continues the bigger grow the hailstones, until finally they become too heavy for even the strongest updrafts and fall all the way to the ground.

It is unusual for hail to grow bigger than the size of a grape, but on rare occasions hailstones have been seen bigger than baseballs and weighing more than a pound and a half. In June 1954 hailstones up to "fifteen pounds" were reported during a severe storm in Holland, which seems very unlikely. But a hailstone of lethal heft is known to have killed a cow in Annapolis, Maryland, many years ago. Others have killed people all the way from America to Asia, where an especially disastrous hailstorm accounted for about 200 deaths at Moradabad, India, on April 30, 1888. This one was part of a tornado surrounded by heavy discus hail that suddenly whirled through the town, leaving 230 dead and thousands of injured behind it. Although the tornado itself killed two or three dozen persons by smashing their homes, the great majority of the dead were said to have been beaten down by the giant hailstones which, if they were like some record hail picked up in the wakes of American tornadoes, could have been disk-shaped up to ten inches in diameter and three inches thick at the center. Probably formed while spinning rapidly near the growing vortex of the storm, these flying saucers (usually not more than an inch or two in di-

ameter) are such an accepted accompaniment of tornadoes
that some meteorologists theorize that the cooling effect of
their dynamic presence may even be a factor in triggering
off a twister at the start.

The largest ones fall at well over a hundred miles an hour
and must have been cradled in updrafts of equivalent speed
to keep them aloft while they were growing. They have been
observed to hum in the air, about fifteen feet apart, while
smaller stones fall proportionately more slowly, quietly, and
closer together—all the way down to the tiniest soft hail or
graupel which can descend as gently and as densely as snow.

As the speed and flight pattern of hail must be influenced
by its shape, which is created by its adventurous history in
the clouds, which again depends partly on its shape, there is
a delicate interbalance of nature here at work. And one can
get some inkling of its complexities by observing the final
form of the most developed hail after it had landed:
some of the stones being shaped like acorns, saucers, holeless
doughnuts, apples with stems, hourglasses, maces, turtles,
fritters, wavy or warted surfaces that look like chunks of
peanut brittle or odd half-melted jackstones.

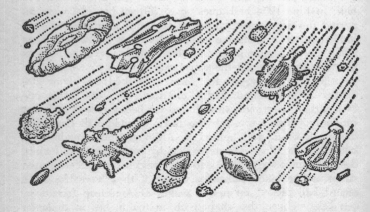

I used to think of clouds as hazy masses of fairly evenly
distributed moisture, and I vaguely imagined that when it
rained the rain was started by the cloud somehow forcing

out its excess water, as you would squeeze a sponge. The truth is rather different.

Rainbirth is a complicated phenomenon that is exceedingly difficult to observe. It is a combination of the slow growth of cloud droplets in humid air and collisions between drops of different sizes or between drops and hail or snow. It is not a mere continuance of the simple saturation process which brings clouds into the world.

A raindrop can be about a million times the size of a cloud droplet which again is larger than an invisible molecule of water vapor by about the same degree. It is an effort therefore to visualize the microscopic flesh structure of the cloud. The tiny droplets that form on dust particles to create a cloud are far apart from each other, actually as far apart in comparison to their size as the earth and the moon. Yet there are so many of them in a cloud that they seem a uniform mass of matter, just as the Milky Way appears to be homogenized rather than a collection of separate stars.

Each cloud droplet may be less than 1/10,000 of an inch in diameter, yet it is floating independently on many millions of bubbling molecules of air like cream on milk, dancing in the sky, ever changing with temperature, pressure, and humidity. As humidity increases or temperature decreases, the size of the droplet grows, more and more moisture condensing on its surface, increasing its weight in relation to surface resistance until the air can no longer hold it up and it accelerates to an appreciable speed of falling.

When the droplet attains to about 1/200 of an inch in diameter it is likely to descend as gentle mist. At 1/50 of an inch it falls as light rain. In falling it is bound to collide with other drops and often ice in some form. If there is little wind and the drops are all of the same size, however, they will fall at about the same speed like cars moving down a highway in file, thus avoiding bumping into one another. In this case the drops do not get very big and the earth receives no more than a drizzle. This is what normally comes from a thin stratus cloud on a calm day.

But when wind currents mix up drops of different sizes so that they fall at different speeds as in a thundercloud, the bigger drops will hit smaller, slower ones while trying to

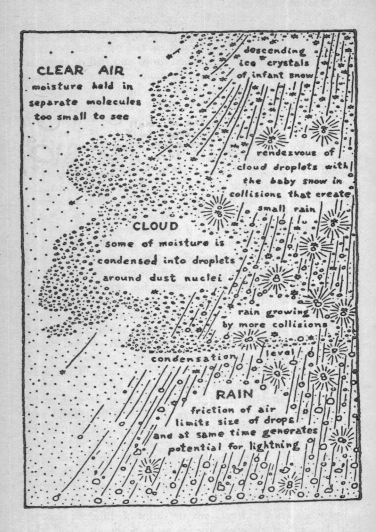

pass them. Thus they will combine together into bigger and bigger drops.

The biggest known raindrops are slightly less than a quarter inch in diameter—or would be if they were round. Actually they are seldom spherical, nor do they look in the air like the traditional "tear drops" you see in cartoons. High-speed flash photographs show instead that once they have

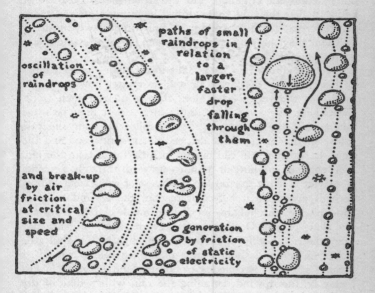

reached falling equilibrium they are flattened out at the bottom into a modified parachute shape that is the almost exact replica of a hamburger bun. This turns out to be nature's compromise between surface tension, which would keep them perfectly round, and the aerodynamic pressure of passing air which pushes against their bellies and sucks out their flanks to a degree that literally tears them apart if they reach the quarter-inch limit.

It is only while they remain tiny droplets of cloud or fog, therefore, that the aerodynamic pressures stay virtually nil and they float like perfect globes upon the air. For as soon as they start to grow and fall their instability increases geometrically with size, speed, and the air's turbulence until, oscillating more and more wildly from egg to bun shape, the drops become tattered in the uneven wind, perhaps dish- or doughnut-shaped, and irregular pieces begin flying off into their wakes of spray.

This has been found to happen around the airspeed of eighteen miles an hour when friction apparently breaches rain's hydrostatic equation. The discarded pieces meanwhile, being smaller than the main drops, have more air resistance in proportion to their weight, so fall more slowly until by collision they in turn may approach a quarter-inch size again, repeating the cycle.

Thus mercifully rain never falls faster than eighteen miles an hour through the lower air and no matter how numerous the drops they cannot be more than a quarter inch thick. Even when the swift downdrafts in a storm may lash the rain against the ground at seventy miles an hour the rule holds, for the 18 m.p.h. is airspeed not groundspeed and the storm-lashed rain still can move but little faster than the air.

A chimney of hot air puffing upward through a cloud, moreover, is likely to stop the mightiest of rains from falling, perhaps evaporate it before it reaches the ground as often happens over the Sahara—for indeed much of rain is for the sky alone to see. Or this great flowering puff of heat may carry the rain bodily upward to brandish it in the chill attic of heaven before dashing it later all at once upon our heads.

Such a torrent is called a cloudburst and happens in just that way, the upwind damming the rain with a dike of dry air, balancing it magically aloft in the volatile tub of sky for many precarious minutes before the downwind bursts the bottom out to trigger the deluge.

One day in November 1911 a weather station at Panama recorded a fall of "2.47 inches of rain during three minutes" of severe thunderstorm. Where there is not enough vegetation to absorb it such a cloudburst can be disastrous. I was in Los Angeles recently when a sudden rain drowned twenty persons in the city streets, some of them under overturned cars. And in July 1911 in the Philippines a terrific downpour is reported to have dumped forty-six inches of rain on the town of Baguio in twenty-four hours. I don't know how much damage the Baguionos suffered but the cloudburst is credited with being the heaviest measured rainfall for a single day in history.

Harder to understand than the most violent irregularities of the rain are the invisible workings of evaporation that can make a cloud vanish like magic into "empty" air. The cloud, as we have said, holds its water condensed into tiny droplets perhaps a thousandth of an inch in diameter and a fortieth of an inch apart but when the cloud evaporates, this moisture suddenly breaks up into separate molecules and disperses itself evenly throughout the whole space available, becoming thousands of times greater in volume than the condensed droplets alone, and spread out so thin it will not refract light and you can see right through it.

It is as if you were flying at 10,000 feet over a great plain upon which thousands of compact companies of soldiers were gathered, each company composed of a hundred men dressed in white uniforms and standing at attention shoulder to shoulder, the companies two hundred and fifty feet apart in all directions. The dots of condensed white would be visible down there, blending in the distance into a faint but vast cloud of humanity. Yet if, at a signal, all the groups suddenly disbanded into individual men, leaving twenty-five feet between each soldier and the next, the cloud of humanity would literally evaporate into invisibility.

It is in exactly this way that sky clouds evaporate by *un*condensation, by the scattering of collected moisture back into its elementary parts. And the same holds true of course in the case of water evaporating from the ocean, or from grass or trees—an almost continuous process everywhere there is air. The average oak tree, I am told, evaporates 180 gallons of water a day while in leaf, and there are calculated to be 16,000,000 tons of water evaporated each second from the whole earth.

The air that absorbs this moisture, far from being burdened as you might think, actually expands and becomes lighter, for water vapor is only five-eighths as dense as dry air—so the water rises faster than the drought, bringing vital raw material right up to the cloud factory levels—great invisible rivers continuously flowing up from the land and sea, dispersing through the sky, condensing and pouring back down again as if to pump and circulate their life-giving juice through the body of the planet.

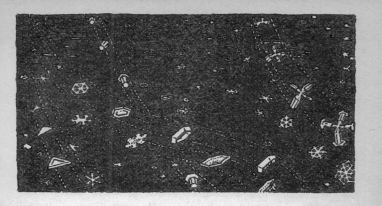

8

The Snow

LOOKING OUT on the occasional snow flurries we inevitably encounter in this winter's crossing, I think of my first visit to the earth's ice age. For that is what the Greenland icecap really is: the last large remnant of the most recent ice age that covered the whole northern half of North America and Europe only thirty or forty thousand years ago. Approaching Greenland at 12,000 feet, riding a four-ton cargo of meteorological equipment one morning in 1944, I saw a range of spectacular mountains with a long flat cloud resting on top. It was apparently a very smooth crest cloud like the white "tablecloth" of Table Mountain in South Africa and it lay there snug and still. But when I looked again I suddenly realized that this was really no cloud at all—not even part of the sky but part of the earth. It was the great Greenland icecap! It was the southern tip of that famous shining mattress of ice more than a mile thick and a thousand miles long that staggers the imagination and far outshines the North Pole region itself for sheer bulk and majesty. Beset by the frigid descending fall winds that are an unsung wonder of the world, and continuously weighted down by new snow, this great ice field is expanding ever outward in all directions at a rate

129

which in places reaches 125 feet a day (an inch a minute)—
a bed of snow that blankets jagged 10,000-foot mountains so
that they are completely smothered from view—great-grand-
mother of the icebergs which are born daily in its hundred
fiords, crashing roughshod from the crumbling childbed glaciers into the ocean to drift downward to the shipping lanes
of the earth.

The snow fields were very treacherous to airplanes until
radar gave us the absolute altimeter, for it was almost impossible before then to judge distance when flying above that
unbroken whiteness. It is a deceptive whiteness—often called
the "whiteout"—that sometimes seems to move along with
the airplane—sometimes slightly faster, sometimes slower—
sometimes appears half a mile below you when it is really
fifty feet, and on occasion has been known to rise up in a
mad blurry rush till two great white plumes appear on either
side of your cockpit and you rock to a sizzling stop, discovering you have flown into the icecap.

In one rare case described to me by Colonel Norman
Vaughan, director of Search and Rescue in the North Atlantic in World War II, a plane flew into a fall of fresh feathery
snow that stopped it so gently that for several minutes the
crew thought they were still flying, although the airspeed
needle had quietly swung to zero and they were in reality
nestled firmly in snow so deep the steady-cruising propellers
had blasted great ten-foot furrows for half a mile and the
fuselage was buried almost to the windows.

Snow's real home of course is in our upper sky where one
must go upon wings to see it. Up there it is always snowing
somewhere and there is always snow—even snow that sleeps,
small snow that rests year upon year on the strong blue
molecules of sky, snow that never comes down. Spawned in
the crystal tail of the white mare, nurtured in the celestial
seas of the silver mackerel, these tiny flakes just float and
float, shimmering in the sun by day, fluttering now upward

to ring the moon, now downward to feed the rain, now northward to doze in arctic silence o'er the pole.

But how are snow flakes born? Whence the ancient treasures of the snow?

Snow in truth is frozen invisible water vapor formed directly in air so cold that the vapor has no chance to turn liquid during its transformation to solid ice. This process that occurs unseen in the great secret heights of the sky is so literally sublime that science has named it sublimation.

Sublimation of water vapor can happen only when it is colder than about 20° F. below zero. In very clean upper air it has to be nearly 60° F. below or colder. An invisible particle of salt or dust or maybe a dry spore floats amid vapor and suddenly, like the mystery of life, becomes the heart of a new crystal, a fertilized ovum of potentiality, the beginning of a snowstorm.

Some scientists think that such a snow germ can be born spontaneously without any foreign nucleus at all, but it is hard to prove. In any case the tiny crystal grows symmetrically in free air with magical wonder. Even when born wrapped in a cloud, the evidence is that it springs direct from the clear vapor between the condensed droplets, moving freely between them like a comet between the stars, growing with the stuff it passes.

The baby snow does not grow at random, however, but is raised very strictly under the prim "law of crystal lattices," which explains hexagonal symmetry: 2 atoms of hydrogen plus 1 atom of oxygen makes 3 atoms that form a molecule of H_2O with a basic triangular tendency that develops into the hexagon—an innate waltz-time attitude toward the world of white and the water crystal, three on three, six on six—air and cloud and snow. It is true that a mysterious cubic or four-sided rhombohedral ice has recently been discovered that seems somehow to defy the law of H_2O crystallization. It may be a hydrate, but until science explains it we must consider it just an anomaly in the hexagonal world of snow.

Starting as a submicroscopic three-dimensional triangle or hollow prism, the normal ice seed always shoots out crystal ice buds at angles of 60° in any direction, solidifying water vapor as it finds it, grabbing molecules as they come, three at a time, half a dozen at a clip. Rapidly the prism thus becomes the axle or hub of a three- or six-sided wheel, which may assume any shape so long as it repeats its pattern to the tune of three. Some turn into hourglasses, scrolls, pyramids, crosses. In high cirrus clouds which are cold and dry the hub usually remains as a bluish cylinder or hollow bullet with minor branches growing only slowly, the whole retaining a compact prismatic or hexagonal spool-like form. But in warmer, moister air or lower clouds it will grow faster, the

some basic forms of snow crystals which grow and combine in the sky, becoming snowflakes that may eventually reach the earth

hub alone remaining short while the six spokes at each end develop complicated barbs and barbules, forming a thin, flat double wheel of wondrous lateral symmetry, occasionally 12-spoked, slowly combining into a solid, greenish disk, sometimes a hexagonal whiskey glass or a jackstone shape which may be also lacy or star-pointed.

The five commonest snow spool motifs are said to suggest the needle, feather, tree, cup, and plate, but all these varied snow types repeatedly fold their crystals around the air as they grow, thereby creating minute hollow tubes which appear as delicate systems of dark dots, rods, and branching lines under the microscope. So individual and charmingly imaginative are these markings and shapes inside a snowflake that you can almost see the merry snow angels up there falling over themselves thinking up new designs for these most exquisite creations of heaven, no two of which have ever been found quite alike.

Though the lateral symmetry of a snow crystal is often as perfect as is a well-made wheel, the two ends of the hub (as in the wheel) are almost always of different sizes, which gives the whole the semblance of a tiny parachute, sometimes a double parachute. And this crystal parachute is functional, for the flake always falls with the hub's small end downward, leaving it slightly convex upward. Some kinds even grow spicules converging downward like the shroud lines of parachutes, which, if the flake falls long enough through moist air, meet at a bottom point and eventually fill the enclosed space with crystalline structure, creating the pellet known as graupel.

In one way or another all of these crystals spin and spiral as they parachute down the sky, now rising on the wind's whim, now settling in its lull—ever changing or growing with the passing invisible vapor, their very shape a perfect record of their journey from the cirrus kingdom, their little spicate branches by their pattern preserving their history of the layers of moisture and temperature through which they have traveled. The main branches grow faster in the more saturated layers of sky while the lesser twigs sprout in the drier spells, eventually whole colonies of related limbs from many sources making up one mature crystal, a sort of patriarchal system arrayed around the six sons of the single common ancestor still seated in his central throne.

Like most of the sky's snow, which never comes to earth at all, even the few flakes destined to reach the ground linger interminably on their downward journey—in some cases taking weeks or months on the way, seldom less than many hours. Their start, as with infant rain, is very slow. It is only after the single crystals have grown big enough to have reasonable chances of colliding with each other that they begin to make noticeable downward progress, collecting gradually into double and triple parachutes, capturing splinters from passing damaged flakes, building colonies of spools and spicules and outwardly irregular tree masses, and finally the great soggy conglomerations we see in heavy flurries, which may reach more than an inch in diameter by the time they come to rest on earth.

As you may have noticed, these falling snowflakes spiral in a number of different ways. Some float almost straight down without turning. Some spin rapidly like propellers. Some twist clockwise; others counterclockwise. Some rotate alternately one way then the other, a few with a flapping motion like a wounded bird or a falling leaf—each a unit of graceful individual expression until its dance is cut impersonally short by the ground.

Delicate and ephemeral as snow often is and beautiful its silent fall, its collective mass is not always just a sweet frosting on the cake of earth, for it can strangle New York City's transportation system in half a night. Sixty-one inches once fell in a single day at Giant Forest, California, and 884 inches (74 feet) in one winter at Tamarack, California. In Calumet, Michigan, which might be called a home of snow, it snowed daily for fifty-one consecutive days from November 1950 to January 1951.

Heavy snowfalls are often very hard to predict for they depend on complex combinations of factors in the impulsive snow factories of the sky. One of the few generalities to be made is that the heaviest snowfalls usually come when the wind has had a long fetch over water or when its veering so matches the movement of the storm center that the precipitation sector of the storm is held over one spot a long time.

It might be appropriate to end this interlude about earthly winter with mention of snow's curious similarity to feathers. This similarity is particularly noticeable with the large multiple flakes whose many crystals seem to be held together after collision in flight by a microscopic zipper action. The fine hexagonal crystals indeed are comparable to barbules and barbicels in that they hook into each other, I've noticed, with a grip strong enough to turn a snow-swept chicken-wire fence into a solid mat of snow resembling a feathered wall, to bridge the gap between swaying clotheslines a foot apart and lock them into a single system, or even to balance such a tonnage of weight on delicate telephone wires that the foot-thick poles holding them up break and collapse to the ground.

Like feathers, snow also makes fine insulation, and the primitive snow-block igloo is one of the world's best-insulated houses. I once measured the temperature of the ground under a foot of feathery snow and found it 44° F. warmer than the air above.

This downy stuff may be literally the flesh of the lower cirrus clouds that somehow got sucked downward and fluttered long enough in very dry air to reach the earth. At any rate its crystals are lacelike and hollow and the snow they make is virtually nothing but air. One part water to twenty parts of air makes a light snow, but some gossamerlike snow tested in Finland was found to contain as little as one part water to three hundred parts of air. That must have been ghosty stuff indeed, for twenty-five feet of it would melt down into only one inch of water!

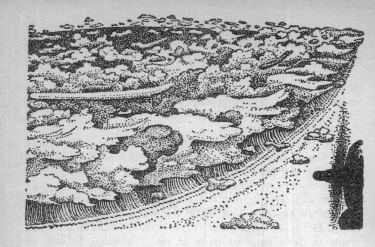

9

The Wine of Weather

IN A ROUTINE CHECK of my instruments at 01:00 G.M.T. I noticed that the temperature had suddenly risen about six degrees to +8° F. And I could no longer see any stars. The difference in altimeter readings showed a corresponding increase in barometric pressure, indicating a stronger drift to the left.

What did these things add up to?

Until the last quarter century they would have suggested much more than a warm southerly wind with perhaps its hint of an early spring. But now the implications were vastly greater. In fact they had taken on a whole new dimension. For it was quite obvious we had just passed a warm front. All the evidence was there on the instruments, with the high overcast to verify it.

"What's the weather going to do?" a voice at my elbow asked. It was Co-pilot Dropford returning from the cabin with his customary two paper cups of coffee: one for himself, one for the captain.

"Just a weak warm front," I replied. "A little air up from Spain. Maybe a shower. But it won't last long."

In some ways, I suppose, it is easier for us than the weather men to see the truth of weather, because we know it more with our eyes than with our minds: we see it with a bird's perspective, flying alternately above and up to our eyes in it. Almost at once do we view the approaching storm and the rainbow behind it.

But what of the new basic weather concepts that are beginning to affect our daily speech, and where did they come from? What is the matter with Ben Franklin's old discovery that weather just rolls along, hitting Philadelphia this evening, New York at midnight, Boston at dawn?

The trouble with the old weather ideas that prevailed until the age of flying came into its own after World War I is that they were two-dimensional. They took into consideration latitude and longitude and vast areas of land and sea but ignored the third dimension of height and the volume and shape of the masses of air that move about the earth.

The principal discoverer of the modern air-mass concept was the great Norwegian physicist, Vilhelm Bjerknes. Standing up there amid the mountains near the very top of the world, he saw something that others had missed. He conceived the simple truth that the weather moves around the earth in great waves thousands of miles apart. Using small free balloons that carry instruments and checking them with airplane reports, he proved that air in the sky circulates in distinct chunks or masses with definite boundaries which have now come to be known as fronts. He made people realize that they are like fish in an aquarium tank with an attendant (God) to change their water (air) at regular intervals, that a complete fresh bath of air literally engulfs our temperate world every few days.

Before Bjerknes, people assumed that air was just air and,

like well-stirred soup, that all parts of it blended imperceptibly into one another to make a homogeneous broth of sky. That theory seemed reasonable enough except that it could not explain how a warm, soggy, misty night would suddenly change to a cold clear, crisp dawn, or why winter always comes in jerks: three days cold and clear, two days damp and thawing, one day of snow followed by five days of cold and clear, three days cloudy and warm, two days cold and clear . . .

Now that Bjerknes has opened the gate, of course, it all seems basically understandable, even obvious. That warm, soggy, misty air did not change miraculously into cold, clear, crisp air. It simply moved a hundred miles farther east and was replaced by new air of a different kind.

But how come the air is arranged in packages of different sorts? What are these airs like? Where do they hail from and whither are they bound?

You know many of them from daily experience: from looking through them, sniffing them, breathing them.

Take the common clear, cool, dry air of the northern and eastern parts of America. It is brisk and bracing and feels newly washed, spiced with spruce and pine and crisp as snow. It should be exactly that way for it has just arrived from Canada where it drifted slowly for weeks among snow-capped mountains over dry northern plains and evergreen forests and cold sparkling lakes. That particular brand of air is called by weather men Polar Canadian or Polar Continental. It sweeps down over the Dakotas and the Great Lakes to New York and New England in intermittent waves, cold and clear and dry from the ground up to the thin stratosphere—waves that may be two or three thousand miles and a full week from crest to crest—waves containing fifty million cubic miles of air in one chunk.

Now what about the air that is between those waves of Polar Canadian air? That is the familiar warm, steamy brand of air that comes in on a southwest wind with a flavor of the Gulf of Mexico and sultry tropical thunderstorms. The weather men label that Tropical Gulf or Tropical Maritime air, for it is fresh from the Spanish Main or the shores of Texas and Louisiana. As it sweeps up the Mississippi Valley between the cold waves, men pull off their wool shirts and long underwear, buds appear on the trees, and the birds flit about with thoughts of mating.

Besides these two best-known American airs, there is the Polar Pacific air that comes from Siberia, picking up moisture off the Aleutians and bringing rain to Seattle. There is the Polar Atlantic air that descends on Nova Scotia and New England as a nor'easter bringing cold rain and the salty tang of the Grand Banks. There is the Tropical Pacific air out of the South Seas that means sunshine in Southern California, and the dry Tropical Continental air off the hot deserts of Mexico and Arizona that blows the sonora northward in summer and may threaten a new dust bowl in Kansas.

Airs, like wines, can be recognized by their taste, color, and quality—by all sorts of subtle manifestations of character. Some airs are milky and mild, some glassy green, some clear as crystal. Every combination of humidity and warmth, of dryness and coolth, is found in some one of the earth's airs. And each has also its own quality of life, sheds its own light, produces its own dew or frost or halos around the moon, has its own distinctive way of moving, its particular treatment of clouds and smoke.

Connoisseurs can often tell a brand of air by one glance at the smoke pouring from a chimney. Smoke is perhaps the most sensitive of signs in the material world. In still, sultry air it will creep lazily forth, in lively, cold air it will bubble and boil, in hurricane air it will be whisked to leeward in wide streamers, in inverted air it will float neatly in layers. Like a cat's tail the very angle and wave motion of the mounting appendage expresses character and mood. Each wisp, each peristaltic furrow flows out as a kind of writing, a nephic soul script that only those who think to the rhythms of the wind can begin to understand.

Sometimes the outward dress of the air changes as it moves over the countryside so that it is hard to recognize where it came from. Tropical Maritime air for example, when it sweeps northward across the United States in winter, leaves Florida like a sparkling summer morning. But over the cold hills of Tennessee and Kentucky it starts condensing so that it arrives at Detroit a dark drizzling mass, and hats and mouths turn down at the corners as people look upon the dismal winter day. One might liken it to a girl in a blue silk bathing suit who puts on an old brown overcoat when coming north. Although she looks very different now she is really still the same girl.

However, not only may a *single* air mass dress oppositely in *different* kinds of country: a *single* country may influence *different* air masses to dress just as oppositely. An example of this might be a stretch of flat Iowa cornbelt thawing in spring. As a wave of cold Polar Canadian air pours over it, it feels warm to the bottom level of the wave which, as it heats, begins to expand, becomes bottom-light and unstable until rising columns of it sprout into vertical puffs of cumulus cloud and moil upward into the paths of airliners whose passengers soon feel queasy and complain about the bumpy weather. But to a following wave of hot Tropical Maritime air that same Iowa farmland feels chilly and the lower level of hot air cools off instead of warming, contracts to become bottom-heavy and stable, leaving the whole air mass floating comfortably in nice horizontal layers of stratus and altostratus cloud, while air passengers can sleep all the way to Denver.

This kind of difference is what keeps weather from being simple and weather forecasters from sleeping nights. The combined and changing factors of temperature, humidity, pressure, and motion over irregular land and sea produce all the kinds of clouds and weather in the world: from the eerie stillness of the arctic where often neither vertical nor horizontal cloud is seen to the dramatic celaje cloudscapes of Guatemala where flat-lens clouds commonly float among giant cumulus, complete stability and peace right next door to explosive uncertainty!

The weather men seek to keep perpetual track of all these goings on in the sky by measuring what factors they can with instruments, some of them dating back to very primitive times. The hygrometer, which measures humidity by the expansion and contraction of human hair, may have been inspired by American Indians who had a saying "When the hair turns damp in the scalp house look out for rain." The thermometer is a result of one of Galileo's mercurial experiments; the barometer the brainchild of Torricelli, first human to stake his reputation on the reality of air.

The greatest of the newer instruments are the basic radiosonde and the now widely used radar. The little radiosonde balloons already are climbing the skies to check the upper air over much of the world by day and through the dead of night. They carry small boxes containing a miniature radio attached to a thermometer and simple moisture meter suspended from a five-foot balloon—man-made questionmarks that rise humbly toward heaven as if to inquire of God His will for today and tomorrow.

The answer comes back by theodolite and by an ethereal radio signal chattering steadily for the hour it takes the balloon to reach the stratosphere and burst. It tells the trained weather man what kind of clouds are forming up there, at what height they are, which way they are developing, and the speed and direction of the wind.

By such and sundry educated probings with a little slide-rule thermodynamics, the weather office maps the sky and is learning within reasonable limits what to expect over desert or sea or forest or arctic ice. It has discovered that some of the hottest and coldest parts of the earth are respectively far from the equator and the poles: the official heat record 134° F. in the shade in Death Valley, California, 36° North Latitude, until it was beaten recently by 136° F. in Azizia, Libya, at 25° North; the official northern hemisphere record for cold —93° F. (unofficially —108° in 1938) at Oimyakon, Siberia, at only 63° North Latitude or parallel with mid-Sweden, while a scientific outpost manned by Russians recorded —114° F. in central Antarctica in 1958.

They say that a noticeable difference between temperatures above and below —100° F. is that when it gets down to about 100° below, horses' heads start to freeze and it becomes risky to let them stand out-of-doors. Their frozen breath may also become a problem and I have seen a Siberian pony standing in a railroad station on the Trans-Siberian in midwinter with an icicle literally reaching from his nose to the ground so that he could have leaned on it.

Perhaps more surprising than surface differences is the fact that at the altitude of twelve miles it averages fifty degrees colder over the equator than over the poles where the warmer stratosphere begins only five miles up. The extreme spread at the surface, however, is actually as great as the difference between freezing and boiling, between ice and steam (Oimyakon is said to have had it as high as +104° F. in summer), and it is mainly nature's effort to equalize or balance this disparity of at least 212° (at most about 250°) that drives the winds and makes the weather.

In order to forecast weather many things are thus taken into consideration: behavior of clouds, temperature, humidity, pressure . . . But the single most essential factor is now recognized to be the air mass. One must know its nature and reactions to the country, and most especially its boundaries, the seams of the atmosphere, the fronts that mark the end of one air mass and the beginning of another.

For these drifting, twisting sky seams are where the most significant weather is found, and recognizing them and analyzing their behavior is the main work of the modern meteorologist. This is called frontal analysis. It is the greatest part of Vilhelm Bjerknes' gift to the world.

Fronts are pretty easy to spot, once you know what you're looking for. They are a sudden change of air bringing a distinct rise or drop in temperature, a wind shift, different humidity, and a new aspect to the whole sky. In an hour from the ground—or in five minutes' flying—you will see the low soggy clouds disperse and the dull gray shroud overhead change to clear, cool blue. It seldom takes much longer for a cold front to pass.

Often the actual air boundary is drawn for you in a line of clouds straight across the entire visible world. It may be a row of thunderstorms, a line squall with roll scud clouds scooting like freight rollers close to the ground before it, or just a slight cumulus demarcation. When flying you will certainly notice the drop on your thermometer, the swing in your driftmeter, and the radically changing clues of wind.

Since cold air is denser and heavier than warm air, a moving mass of cold air naturally hugs the ground—and it moves forward at first underneath the warmer air it is replacing, prying it up and pushing it back as you might raise an old board with your boot and kick it away. A cold front cross section, like the cold air under a thunderstorm, is in fact shaped almost exactly like a boot, the rounded toe rising perhaps twenty thousand feet high, followed by a wedgelike foot sloping gradually up to forty thousand feet and more.

An hour or so before the toe of cold air arrives at any one spot, the clouds there can feel the warm air rising and shying away from the approaching boot. Their nervous motion at this time is like a bunch of horses before a prairie fire —the fire of rising heat bubbles disturbed by pressure. Otherwise there isn't much warning. The air feels as warm and moist as ever, the wind still mostly south.

Then it strikes! Big cumulus clouds appear to the northwest—feminine cumulus thunderheads with beautiful, treacherous curves. They may look light and gay up top, but will turn out to be darker and more threatening in the middle. In summer they are spiced with lightning.

This rolling bank of clouds is the actual forward edge of the advancing cold air, the toe of the boot—held back a little by scuffing friction at the ground but bulging forward angrily to kick the warm air up and away. At the moment of impact there is sudden rain, often a cloudburst, the cold shock condensing the moisture far beyond the air's capacity to hold it. Then the full mass of cold air surges in from the northwest in gusts. Sometimes it is a squall vicious enough to tear shingles from roofs, topple trees, or flip taxiing airplanes over on their backs.

In a half hour the hurly-burly is done, the rain stopping, the Dutchman's breeches showing blue. The front is passed. The new air mass has swallowed the whole sky and you can reasonably expect "air mass weather" for a while—at least weather characteristic of this particular kind of air mass until some new front announces another change of air.

The next front could be another one still colder, but it is five times more likely to be a warm one, bringing Tropical Maritime air of some sort. Warm fronts are easier to forecast because they send messengers days ahead of themselves, envoys of high flying cirrus to tip off weather men, farmers, or sailors. This the source of the adage: "Mare's tails and mackerel scales make lofty ships carry low sails."

As warm air is light, the shape of a warm front is very different from the heavy scuffing boot of the cold front. Instead of coming in low, its leading edge rides high and is shaped in cross-section like a ski—the long light ski of a jumper landing: the forward end of the ski well off the ground, the trailing end just touching.

This warm-front sky ski is a thousand miles long, two or three times as long as the cold-front boot. Its forward curved top over Boston is made of curly cirrus clouds 30,000 feet high, feathers of snow appropriate to skiing. Along its straight length is the usual sequence of descending clouds: cirro-stratus the milk cloud at 20,000 feet over Pittsburgh, alto-stratus the sheet cloud at 12,000 feet over Columbus, nimbo-stratus the drizzle cloud at 5000 feet over Indianapolis in a mood to drag its feet there with light rain for several days, possibly mist or fog.

As indicated in the aphorism "Rain long foretold, long last; short notice, soon past," the easy warm bath of the warm front is a long-acoming, long-agoing, lackadaisical affair—in contrast to the short and snappy cold shower of the cold front. When its soggy clouds finally break up, the wind will be found to have swung toward the south and the weather will persist warm and humid—until the next air mass arrives.

And so goes the air-mass cycle—cold and dry, warm and humid, cold and dry, colder and drier, warm and dry, cold and damp, warm and humid, cold and dry . . . There is a rhythm to it—certainly a repetition, if somewhat irregular. The great air waves come along in an unending procession. They don't all hit the same spots and are of very different shapes and sizes—their storms sometimes misleading like the instability line of squalls that often precedes a cold mass at ground level by many hours, their fronts sometimes almost unrecognizably weak or washed out or straggling—just as waves of water or waves of birds flying or waves of trees in a forest. But they keep on coming, following natural laws, until you can learn to understand them, to anticipate them some.

It is a little as though you were a snail clinging to a rock at the edge of the sea where the surf was coming in so that you were under water about as often as out. Each wave would hit you a little differently, some bigger, some smaller, some foamier, some saltier, some spaced far apart, some close upon the one before.

It would be next to impossible to predict reliably whether

you would be in water or air at exactly one minute hence—
yet you'd have a pretty good idea of the situation of five seconds hence, maybe ten seconds hence. That is how it is with
the weather man: he can see the waves coming plainly
enough, but telling exactly when, how, and where they will
strike is another thing again.

The United States Weather Bureau with some five hundred stations, no doubt the best equipped and most exten-
sive synoptic meteorological organization in the world, is
said to attain only about eighty-five per cent accuracy of
forecast. To a wave of air three thousand miles wide, the
U.S. Weather Bureau bears just about the same relation as a
bunch of snails to an ocean wave.

The motive force behind both kinds of waves is the same:
the sun's heat and the earth's motion. Chapter 5 told of the
basic wind circulation of the earth in which heated tropical
air rises and flows poleward to replace cold, settling polar air
being sucked equatorward to replace rising tropical air
flowing poleward . . . This general flow, however, is im-
mensely complicated by the coriolis force of the earth's turning and the wrinkles of the world's skin: the monsoon effect
of summer sea winds and winter land winds, the barriers of
mountains, the up and down drafts over gulfs and plains.

And amid all this complex dynamic flowing of winds, of
doldrums and horse latitudes, one of the great meteorological
discoveries was made about the year 1917: the polar front.
Although four out of every five persons on earth lives on a
polar front, no one had realized it or comprehended the
front until the genius of Bjerknes brought it to light. The
polar front is the superfront or permanent zone of warm and
cold fronts. It is the main traffic intersection between
warmed tropical air flowing north and cooled polar air
flowing south. It is where the low pressure storms roll counterclockwise between the clockwise-turning high-pressure
masses, like ball bearings between wheels in an engine. It is
the great crossroads of the sky—to some extent a social circle,

a mixing hall, or a prize ring. Bjerknes called it a front because this belt of continuous conflict between different airs
reminded him of the battlefronts of the great war that was
still going on.

In the Southern Hemisphere where west winds can blow
clean around the world without obstruction between the
Andes and Antarctica, the polar front is fairly simple and
confines itself largely to the uninhabited band of the graybeards and the albatross between south latitudes 50° and
6°.

But in the Northern Hemisphere, which is interspersed
with the eggbeater action of jagged Rocky Mountains,
Greenland's icecap, Norwegian fiords, and the Himalayas,
the story is different. Here the polar front doesn't go just
through the Bering Sea, Hudson Bay, and so on around the
subarctic world but swashes and splashes over the whole
temperate zone from Mexico to Alaska, from Arabia to Norway. Of course semi-tropical places such as Florida and
Egypt and Formosa are beyond the reach of most of the
waves. They are like seabirds sitting on a cliff: they get only
an occasional lash of spray from the huge combers that
march steadily across the northern United States and Canada, northern Europe, Siberia and Japan. The crests of these
main waves average about three thousand miles apart, so
that it takes only six of them to ring the earth at latitude
50°, but there are smaller wavelets corrugating the surfaces
of the big waves, a mere thousand miles or so apart, often
overtaking each other (occluded fronts), often curling at
their crests (large storm areas) like white-caps on the sea,
reaching too high for stability, breaking and dissolving into
islands of foam (dwindling rain areas). These are the assorted, squirming little cold and warm fronts we've been describing that hit Chicago and Berlin and Tokyo two or three
times a week. They are the minor waves of the air ocean.

Like all weather, polar front waves move somewhat with
the sun, marching closer to the Arctic Circle in summer, lick-
ing the Tropic of Cancer in winter, parading endlessly eastward around the earth—here fading, there reappearing—their

troughs and crests bringing alternately snow and buds to half the world.

Just how far and fast a single air-pressure wave can continue as a recognizable entity is shown by the fact that the weather men spotted a tiny ripple on the polar front at Havre, Montana, on February 23, 1925, and watched it grow into a giant wave of low pressure, a winter storm swirling steadily eastward, out across the North Atlantic past Iceland to Britain and the Baltic Sea. For a full month they traced it—all the way across Siberia and the North Pacific to Alaska and Canada, past its starting point and on again to the Gulf of St. Lawrence where it melted into another and larger wave on March 23. In twenty-eight days this individual wave of weather had traveled 21,379 miles at an average speed of 32 m.p.h.

Often the advancing boot of low polar air overtakes the light ski of the warm front, undercutting it, closing in and fusing with another polar cold wave that is retreating ahead and below the warm front. This is the occluded front and its complexities were completely baffling before Bjerknes explained air masses. They are still puzzling enough, though more is being learned about them every day, and more about the invisible upper winds, the hidden ringmasters who crack the secret whips of command.

The jet stream of circumpolar vortex, already described as the major wind of the world, is seen in the largest perspec-

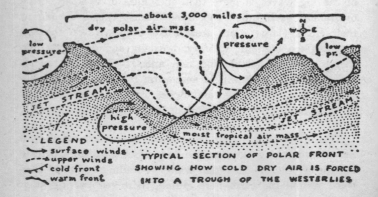

LEGEND
→ surface winds
---→ upper winds
⌢ cold front
〜 warm front

TYPICAL SECTION OF POLAR FRONT
SHOWING HOW COLD DRY AIR IS FORCED
INTO A TROUGH OF THE WESTERLIES

tive as the dominant factor in all regional heat waves or cold waves that pass over the temperate earth. Even the 10,000,000,000 tons of air that twice a year roll across the equator from summer to winter are guided by its changing courses, and it is becoming increasingly important in long-range forecasting as it pulls lower air along in the friction of its wake. Whether it circles the planet in three days of January or in ten days of July, its eddies whirl outward and downward for weeks as cyclonic rains and blizzards, sub-eddies in turn as thunderstorms, and in some cases sub-sub-eddying tornadoes or waterspouts. And associated with it are such newly discovered phenomena as the tropical cold storms that form six miles high and a thousand miles in diameter near the equator—massive disturbances that never come down to earth at all.

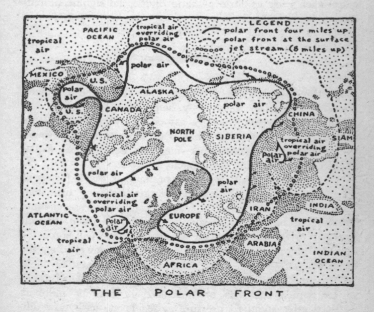

THE POLAR FRONT

If knowledge of the jet stream and the ionosphere above it is the beginning of a greater science of weather, now still as infantile as Keplerian astronomy, there is also a lesser science of weather called microclimatology. This has to do with local atmospheric conditions at airports and on farms, and small-scale weather in general. Orchardists study it to circumvent frost, florists use it to create optimum climates in their greenhouses, manufacturers and air-conditioning engineers, foresters and highway experts keep close tabs on it.

Barnyard climate affecting the health of cattle, pigs, and chickens can be improved by architectural design taking into consideration sun slant, drafts, humidity, insulation . . . Stripping moss off arctic ground in Siberia has enabled the summer sun to thaw large areas deep enough to grow vegetables. Building small windbreaks and mulching as a general farming practice has affected the climate of whole regions, helped turn dust bowls into gardens. Even ant-hills and furrows have their warm, dry sides and their cool, moist sides—each rock its little climatic divide, its significant pattern of pressure areas.

Pressure is an aspect of weather that should be especially considered because it not only helps us keep track of the moving storm areas (usually associated with low pressure and the falling barometer) but is a clue also to such seemingly unrelated phenomena as volcanoes, earthquakes, explosions, tides, swells, and the capacity of wells.

Average or standard sea level pressure is 29.92 inches of mercury, which means that in a large U-shaped tube half filled with mercury, one end sealed up to preserve a vacuum between it and the mercury, the other end open, the air pressing in the open end on an average day will force the level of mercury on that side 29.92 inches lower than the other and airless level. That's the classic barometer invented by Torricelli, and it demonstrates the weight and substance of air, which can also be measured in bars or millibars (1013.2 mbs. standard pressure at sea level) as is now universal practice.

To give yourself some realistic idea of what hefty stuff air is, just remember that the air in a cube-shapéd room thirty feet on each side weighs one full ton, just like a ton of coal. Every square foot of the earth's surface holds up more than a ton of air, which you can imagine as a column a foot thick rising invisibly as high as air is air.

Of course the only reason this column a hundred miles high or so doesn't weigh much more is that the air gets rapidly thinner and lighter as it goes up. But, logically enough, it also gets thicker and heavier as it goes down. In fact air weighs quite a bit more in places hundreds of feet below sea level like Death Valley, and somebody figured out that if miners should dig a mine thirty-five miles straight down they would have trouble keeping track of their shoring lumber, for the boards would float around on the dense air like driftwood on the sea. If the mine were much deeper than that the miners themselves would start to float and the whole project might take on the dreamy atmosphere of the deep sea.

The sensitive relationship between weather and slight changes on the barometer is shown by the fact that the lowest sea-level pressure ever officially recorded on earth was 26.35 inches of mercury on the Florida keys, September 2, 1935. That was less than twelve per cent below normal, yet it took a hurricane to restore the atmosphere to balance again.

Perhaps some otherwise unexplained incidents in history could be caused in part by the psychological effect of low atmospheric pressure, for it has been statistically proved that when the glass is low more accidents occur, more suicide attempts, more crimes, more lovers' quarrels, more babies are born, more packages left in buses, more gloves forgotten, more dogs gone astray.

Temperature and humidity undoubtedly also play their part. In the Bank of England, for instance, they used to have a rule that the important files be locked up during dense fogs because of the mysterious errors that occurred then. Examination marks have been found to be lowest in hot humid weather. Crimes of passion reach a peak in July and August, liquor in summer is more intoxicating, ponderous reading more difficult, memory more slippery.

Someone has even worked out a relationship between changes of air masses and the state of the body, concluding that cold fronts cause contraction of blood vessels, spasms, improved metabolism, and biochemical reduction; warm fronts the opposite.

From my window before the wing I can see at last a little logic in it all. I think I can really see weather in its three dimensions. The cold front hits me like a slanting wall of ice. I watch the rain descending in waves and see the thermometer of outside air drop sharply, the pressure altimeter rising. There is hardly room for doubt as to what is actually going on.

I can see fairly clearly now that rain and snow do not ride in on the wings of a storm as I used to think, but are born locally, sired by the arriving air mass upon its nuptial clash with the retreating maternal air. I can realize why the deserts are generally on the lee sides of great rain-catching mountains.

Even some of the ancient aphorisms take on new sense now. Those swallows dipping low before the rain are catching bugs that can't fly high because of the burden of unusual humidity on their wings. The same must hold for swarming bees and wasps. And the damp air preceding rain naturally sets the frogs to croaking as well as putting a halo around sun and moon and settling the particles of smoke to turn it back to earth. If the drain can be smelt before the storm it is the low pressure releasing gases, and the same low pressure could conceivably explain premonitory creaking bones or corns that ache on the eve of a hurricane.

Seeing the great waves of weather roll by from our new height and speed and knowledge makes me think sometimes of those science movies of sprouting flowers in which hours are condensed into seconds and you are given a God's-eye view of the green shoots literally popping out of the soil and dancing in the sun as their petals and leaves unfold in search of light and fulfillment.

The same treatment may be applied to speeding up slow developments in geology, astronomy, economics, and it has already been used seriously by meteorologists in studying cloud movement.

One such time-lapse movie, for instance, proved to weather students that most cumulus clouds are continuously curling over—rolling so slowly that their true motion had not been comprehended before. Speeded-up thunderheads on the screen were revealed to have a new majesty of explosive rhythm, the successive cumulus towers shooting up at their appointed intervals like puffs of smoke from a steam locomotive, and a steady forward turning of each cloud mass upon the axis of its invisible lower air circulation like a series of great wheels rolling inexorably across the sky.

The weather room is where pilots and navigators get perspective on the atmosphere just before taking off into it. A series of weather maps of the world is in fact a rather exalting spectacle, permitting one a glimpse through a sort of keyhole of the sky. Clouds and continents are spread out like playing cards from outer space.

At Gander in Newfoundland, for instance—the first city in the world to grow up almost wholly on the nourishment of flight—the weather men can show you African weather, Swedish weather, U.S. weather, Greenland weather, Scottish weather, Icelandic, Bermudian, Azorian, even North Pole weather. You get a sense of detachment about the world there. Each man's "weather" is so to speak tailor-made to fit his needs. If you are to take off at midnight, you may be informed casually, "We'll have your weather for you at ten o'clock, sir." It sounds like Saint Christopher speaking to the Angel Gabriel.

Your personal "weather" is handed to you as a neat folder containing at least two large maps. One is a pressure map of isobars and fronts, a bird's-eye view of the world you plan to fly over as it looks from high overhead. The other a cross-section of your course looking horizontally from the side, showing the cloud systems expected en route each at its reported position and height, with symbols in color showing icing conditions, rain or snow or lightning, and the freezing level as a dividing line. With figures for winds in every zone at different altitudes, temperatures, and ceiling and visibility at the terminals, you have the main facts at your fingertips. It should help you keep out of trouble.

But the truth is that there is still a sad dearth of weather information—especially from certain vast areas in which no one lives and airplanes seldom penetrate. All too often the pressure ridges and troughs have moved beyond the realization of the weather office, and wind has radically changed, and conditions are not what the reports have led us to expect.

Rapid closing in of weather in a congested area like New York can be very serious when not forecast accurately. If you were living there in the winter of 1947 you may remember the case of the four-motored American Airlines plane that took off from LaGuardia airport at dusk bound for Los Angeles with twenty-one passengers aboard. The pilot, J. E. Booth, was unable to make his scheduled landing at Washington because of bad weather, so he turned around to try Baltimore, which was reported open. But before he got there, Baltimore also had its ceiling fall below the allowed limits, and Philadelphia likewise folded before he could land. So he returned all the way to New York, only to hear from the LaGuardia tower of heavy snow flurries which had just closed up that airport tight.

As nothing closer was reported available, Booth now headed through the night sky for Westover Field in Massachusetts, but on discovering he had only twenty minutes' gas left turned again, requesting emergency clearance at LaGuardia. When he got down to five minutes' fuel and still couldn't find LaGuardia he requested a radio fix of position. A minute later he saw water below through a hole in the clouds—then a beach. He dropped flares and could just see a park and a level causeway, so he circled and came in to land. Being unable to get more than an occasional glimpse in the darkness and snowy air he overshot, bounced through some scrub grass at the end of the causeway, and luckily came to rest on the sand of Cedar Beach (next to Jones Beach), Long Island. Although he was cut on the head himself, all his passengers were safe.

But the same unpredicted blanket of snow and sleet that had descended on the area for 250 miles around New York that night had trapped another plane bound from Miami to New York. This one, not so lucky, crashed in New Jersey—its co-pilot and two passengers killed, and nearly everyone else aboard seriously injured.

On Wings of Mystery

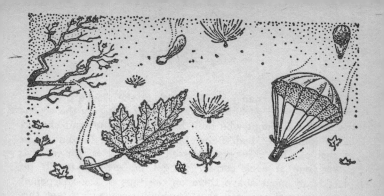

10

Floating on Air

THE SKY has not been easy to explore. Even as I look out my round window at 11,000 feet, I realize that the lower air is about eight hundred times lighter than the water that is the lightest medium below it. Yet many times it has been invaded by beings heavier than itself. For again and again has life risen up from the gentle earth and the sea to dare to fly. And five times it has amply succeeded.

After the very early passive launchings of pollen and spores and tufted seeds came the winged insects nearly a billion years ago in the earth's first active conquest of the air. Second, the ancient pterodactyls and other flying reptiles. Third, the birds. Fourth, the bats. Fifth, man.

Although man's great victory has come largely in my own half lifetime, it is already complete enough to be accepted casually by many professional flyers. But I personally find it hard to share their carefree forgetfulness of the meaning of flight, for it is plain to me that life on earth is suddenly quickening. One generation has leapt off a horse's back and through the sonic wall. Life moves naturally upward in a spiral, but here the spiral is bent strangely, before continuing its accelerating, buoyant course.

It was the Persian poet, Firdausi, in the eleventh century who wrote of an early human attempt at flying by the eccentric Shah Kai Kaoos who built himself a unique craft shaped like a four-poster bed. Being better versed in falconry than mechanics, Kai Kaoos harnessed four eagles for motive power, one at each corner. To get his engines to lift he placed raw meat above them on the tops of the sharpened posts. Firdausi reported that the Shah managed to get this contraption off the ground but had trouble synchronizing his motors and soon had to make a forced landing in the desert from which he was rescued only with the greatest difficulty.

The medieval windmill was another precursor of human flight, providing a close model of the modern four-bladed, square-edged propeller—almost as prenatal human growth reviews human evolution.

The idea of using hot air or gas as a lifting agent seems to have come to many persons during the last four centuries. Leonardo da Vinci is credited with having once made some wafer-thin figures of wax which he filled with hot air and launched into the sky on the occasion of Pope Leo X's coronation.

The Jesuit, Francisco de Lana, designed an aerial sailing ship in 1670 with four copper vacuum spheres to lift it. His theory of buoyancy was remarkably advanced but perhaps he realized that his vacuum spheres could not be both thin enough for lightness and thick enough to withstand the inward pressure of the air, for he never tried to build it.

A few years later in 1709, however, another Jesuit, Bartholomeu de Gusmão, actually sent up a small hot-air balloon and designed a large airship on the hot-air principle which might well have carried him aloft had he had faith or fortune enough to execute his ideas.

In those days the feminine principle of passive, rotund, floating flight was even less understood than the bird-inspired masculine concept of active, flapping flight—yet it was destined to come to glorious fulfillment both soon and suddenly in 1783. That was the famous year when two French brothers in the paper-making craft noticed how a fire wafts pieces of paper upward on its hot clouds of smoke, and they tried filling a paper bag full of the same kind of smoke to see if it would rise too.

It did. Even better than they had expected! And so Joseph and Etienne Montgolfier got started in ballooning. They looked up Priestley's famous treatise on air, and made bigger and bigger bags of hot smoke until on June 5 of that year, feeling confident at last that they had hold of a real discovery, they put on a public ascension before a thousand spectators in the market place of their home town of Annonay, near Lyons.

This first full-size balloon was made of linen and paper, 105 feet in circumference and buttoned together in gores. The Montgolfiers built a fire of straw and wool under it, filling it quickly with thick yellow smoke. Then they cut the cords and it rose impressively for several thousand feet, landing ten minutes later about a mile and a half away.

This demonstration by the Montgolfiers made a tremendous sensation and within a week was the talk of all Europe. The Paris Academy straightaway commissioned its physicist, J. A. C. Charles, to investigate. Professor Charles may have assumed that the balloon's inventors utilized Cavendish's recent discovery of hydrogen, then popularly known as "inflammable air," for he quickly designed his own idea of a hydrogen balloon and had one made thirteen feet in diameter which he set up on the Champ de Mars before a crowd composed largely of "philosophers, officials, students, and loiterers" on August 27. Although it rained that day, the balloon rose on schedule and disappeared into the low clouds. A wag among the open-mouthed spectators just then turned to the aged American ambassador standing near him and asked "Of what use is a balloon, Mr. Franklin?" Replied the famous inventor of the lightning rod, "Of what use, sir, is a new-born baby?"

An hour later some peasants near Gonesse saw a strange globe miraculously descend from the clouds and bounce upon a field. Frightened but fascinated, they gathered around the mysterious buoyant object. When one jabbed it with his pitchfork it hissed forth a dangerous smell, so the others all joined in killing the evil creature with spades and scythes. When nothing remained but shreds, the corpse was dragged off tied to the tail of a horse.

Meanwhile the Montgolfier brothers had come to Paris to demonstrate their hot-air balloon to the Academy. They built a new and fancy one with colorful decorations and pictures on it, which ascended successfully on September 12. By this time people were talking about human travel by balloon, but no one had yet volunteered to try it, so on September 19 the Montgolfiers sent up a large balloon carrying a sheep, cock, and duck to see if life could survive way up there in the unknown.

After the barnyard delegation landed safely a new balloon was built for human passengers and the king wanted to send up two criminals for the first flight, but Pilâtre de Rozier, curator of the Royal Museum of Natural History, persuaded His Majesty that the privilege of being the first human to fly was too rare an honor to waste on a convict, so he and the Marquis d'Arlandes were given the chance. During November they cautiously experimented in the new balloon while it was tethered and at last on November 21 were cut loose on the world's first free human flight!

This momentous event went off smoothly and the balloon rose some 500 feet and drifted five miles over the Bois de Boulogne in plain sight of hundreds of cheering people.

From this date ballooning was accepted throughout the Western world, and Professor Charles completed the first hydrogen balloon of almost modern form in time to take off on December 1 from the Tuileries with a fellow balloon maker named Roberts. This remarkable craft, launched in 1783, still the birth year of ballooning, was complete with rubberized fabric, a net to support the basket, top valve, ballast, and a barometric altimeter. Charles flew all the way to Nesle that time, twenty-seven miles.

Only a year later a balloon crossed the English Channel from Dover to the forest of Guînes in France. Jean-Pierre Blanchard was the first, and among the greatest, of aerial showmen. A "petulant little fellow" around five feet two

inches tall and "well suited for vapourish regions," he made the first ascents in America and in many European countries, and was determined to be the first man to fly the channel. Not having much money, however, he persuaded an American physician, Dr. John Jeffries, to finance the trip. But he tried desperately to prevent the doctor from accompanying him and diluting the glory. He pretended the balloon was not big enough to support them both and secretly wore a lead-lined belt to prove it.

His unpleasant argument with Jeffries was patched up only at the last moment by the Governor of Dover Castle as the two men took off from the white cliffs on January 7, 1785. Their interesting cargo included a barometer (for reading height), a compass, anchors, flags, cork life jackets, thirty pounds of ballast, a packet of pamphlets, a bottle of brandy, biscuits, apples, and the latest in aerial navigation equipment; a large rudder, two big silk-covered sky oars, and Blanchard's famous "moulinet"—a hand-operated revolving fan, which was the first big step upward in the windmill's evolution into the propeller.

They got away safely on a fine northwesterly breeze, but the crossing proved a hair-raising adventure. Evidently the sky was full of cumulus clouds with strong updrafts beneath them and downdrafts between, for the balloon kept rising and falling with bewildering inconsistency until the two men were at their wits' end. One can imagine what the uncontrolled Blanchard muttered to his companion every time the balloon started downward toward the sea. As the balloon moved with the air rather than through it, the rudder was entirely useless, and the oars and moulinet were ridiculously unwieldy and ineffective under the great sluggish hulk of the hydrogen bag.

They had not reached halfway before all the ballast was gone and they had to jettison the anchors, the rudder, oars, moulinet, even the brandy, in order to stay in the air. Just off the French coast the situation looked so desperate that both men, after relieving themselves, started removing their clothes and the panicky Blanchard had just tossed overboard his trousers with a dramatic gesture when an unexpected updraft raised the balloon so high that he nearly froze before they finally descended into the trees twelve miles beyond the coast. The car of the balloon can be seen today in the Calais Museum.

The original Montgolfier or hot-air balloon was within two years almost entirely supplanted by the superior Charlière or hydrogen balloon and ballooning became a widely practiced sport. To what lengths impetuous Frenchmen carried ballooning in the decades that followed cannot be better illustrated than by the duel fought on May 3, 1808, when two emotional gentlemen of Paris blazed away at each other with blunderbusses while drifting in balloons half a mile above the Tuileries Gardens.

Probably the biggest part in history played by balloons was during the siege of Paris in 1870–71 when sixty-six of them evacuated about a hundred important persons, nine tons of mail, and four hundred homing pigeons from the city. At first the balloons took off by day but when a few were nearly shot down by Prussian bullets and shells, night departures became more common. Fifty-nine of these balloons actually succeeded in landing in friendly territory, five fell into enemy hands, and the remaining two were presumed lost at sea. The zeppelins of World War I later also evolved from balloons but balloons have since then, despite their increasing use in meteorology and air-raid defense, faded in importance relative to the airplane.

Before the epic story of the airplane, however, we must take up another earlier invention that developed almost simultaneously with the balloon: the parachute, a natural vehicle of passive flight.

So natural is the parachute in fact that not only have seeds and spores resorted to its principle but many animals have adopted either it or its companion principle of gliding, obviously the prelude to active flight.

The insects were earth's first real flyers, most of them—especially the very small ones—using the parachute idea about as much as the wing to stay aloft. Their very minuteness has made that inevitable for the same reason that the surface of any small object is greater in proportion to its weight (more parachutelike) than that of a larger object of similar shape and material.

You can figure this out mathematically on the basis of simple dimensions. As surface has only two dimensions and weight (like volume) three, so the relationship between surface and weight is proportionately as the square to the cube. Thus a creature loses more weight than surface as he becomes smaller, and it is its *relatively* great surface that gives the little ant enough air resistance to parachute safely any distance. Large beetles can do fairly well in parachuting too. Even a mouse can drop from an airplane without much risk of injury. A rat, however, is usually knocked out. A dog is killed. A man is broken. A horse disintegrates. An elephant splashes.

For this reason specialization in the form of a parachute is unnecessary to any animal smaller than a mouse. But many animals only a little bigger have adopted them in varying degrees from the Malayan umbrella lizard or draco, with his gorgeously colored folding parasol made of fine membrane stretched over actual ribs, to the Bornean glider snakes which can suck their bellies against their backbones and float from tree to tree like ribbons on the wind.

The first human to design a parachute seems to have been the versatile Leonardo about A.D. 1500, but the only actual use for parachutes after his time was in the popular "umbrella dance" often put on by court entertainers who amused their royal patrons with tremendous leaps made possible by big umbrellas attached to their belts.

It was not until the birth year of the balloon, 1783, that the real parachute became an independently proven possibility. In that year Sebastian Lenormand made himself the first full-fledged parachute and jumped with it from the tower of Montpellier Observatory in France. He landed safely but seems to have regarded his apparatus as nothing more than a new means of escaping from fires in tall buildings.

Showman J.-P. Blanchard was the first person to use a parachute in a drop from a balloon. In 1785 he released one from several thousand feet up containing a dog in the basket beneath it. The dog barked on the way down and landed unharmed.

Blanchard still felt uneasy about trying the parachute himself but finally did so eight years later. His primitive parachute either was too small for his weight or swayed very violently for Blanchard hit the ground so hard he broke his leg.

The real father of the parachute is generally considered to be André Jacques Garnerin who had plenty of time to design parachutes while serving a prison sentence in Budapest. Shortly after his release he made his first drop over Paris in 1797, followed by many more descents in other parts of France and England. His chutes oscillated so violently that he would get actively seasick on the way down and usually arrived in no condition to appreciate the raucous enthusiasm of the cheering crowds who wanted to carry him triumphantly on their shoulders.

Garnerin's parachutes were like huge beach umbrellas with a basket hanging below similar to a balloon's car. They were made of canvas about the same size as modern parachutes but inevitably heavier and they must have hit the ground much harder.

The first life saved by parachute was that of a Polish aeronaut named Jordaki Kuparento whose poorly made hot air balloon caught fire over Warsaw in 1808. Luckily he had a parachute aboard, got it opened up in time, and managed to drop to safety.

A few years later Gernerin's niece, Eliza Garnerin, was the first woman parachutist. But there was still a lot of basic experimenting to be done before the parachute would achieve its present perfection, and one of the wide-eyed young spectators of Garnerin's first descent in London, Robert Cocking, was the first to be killed in an attempt to improve on it.

Parachutes were brought into common use by German aviators during the last few months of World War I while the Allied flyers still considered them too bulky and heavy to be worthwhile except in the case of observation balloons which often were shot down several times daily.

But just after the war the seat-pack type of 'chute was generally adopted for its efficiency, weighing only eighteen pounds and replacing the seat cushion so that it carried the aviator instead of the aviator carrying it. More than 1500 experimental jumps were made at the end of the war in perfecting this invention, while literally millions of descents have been made since then in working out the exact parachute procedures used today.

The parachute schools now teach students such long-proven lessons as the headlong dive from open cockpit planes for getting one's head and shoulders away fast. And that after you jump it's important to wait before pulling your ripcord until you have lost your forward speed—especially if you jumped out of a plane traveling several hundred miles an hour, which may well be enough to tear your parachute apart or jerk the harnesses clean off you. Contrary to what you might think, your speed through the air just after jumping is almost certainly decreasing rather than increasing—for at least several seconds—and the faster your plane was moving the more certainly this is true.

The modern manuals explain that you should not dive

with your knees drawn up because that makes you somersault and when you pull the ripcord while somersaulting the lift webs are apt to yank up between your knees, causing you to descend hanging upside down and probably painfully. A British pamphlet says, "a very good view of the ground is at once obtained but the position is extremely uncomfortable, definitely undignified, and you may even lose things out of your pockets."

The American Naval Manual thoughtfully adds: "If one of those things in your pockets happens to be your address book, you'll bewilder the farmer who picks it up and also leave yourself with nothing to do at night but go to the movies. That's hard on your eyes."

Some think that the opening of a parachute after falling for a mile or so must be a terrific jerk but the modern 'chutes have built-in shock absorbers to make your whole ride more comfortable. The silk or nylon canopy is woven loosely enough so that some of the air flows right through it and the remaining trapped air has just enough resistance to slow you up like an automobile with brakes applied, which is much gentler than hitting a stone wall.

The serious swaying that bothered Garnerin and Blanchard so much is virtually impossible in a modern 'chute, and even if you should find yourself swinging a little you can easily eliminate it by pulling on the shroud lines, spilling air out of one side or the other of your canopy. You can change your angle and speed of descent that way too, thus controlling to an important degree where you are going to land.

You should of course have a fair amount of time to work on your landing on the way down. Once it opens, your parachute slows your falling speed to about twenty feet a second —depending on your weight and the density of the air.

The manuals advise jumping from above 1000 feet, and consider it very dangerous to bail out from less than 250 feet. However, a few lucky lads have gotten away with it under desperate circumstances at around 100 feet, which can be taken as the absolute limit below which it's a better bet to stick with your falling aircraft even if it's full of dynamite and heading for a cliff.

In general the higher you are when you jump the better your chances—that is, up to 20,000 feet or so, depending on the conditions of weather and air. Jumps have been made from much higher without ill effects, but above 30,000 feet the shortage of oxygen becomes a problem of first importance. Special oxygen masks and heated pressure suits are now being used in stratospheric parachuting, while several sorts of new capsule cockpits are under development with fins, automatic parachutes and other lifesaving equipment for use after an emergency ejection even from a rocket in space.

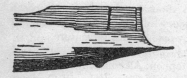

A key principle in the evolution of all these devices for controlling a fall through the atmosphere is the *terminal velocity* any object reaches after several seconds of falling—a kind of fixed speed the body attains after its accelerating (or decelerating) resistance to the air has reached final equilibrium with gravity. It is a kind of peaceful balance of nature long known to bugs but just recently discovered by man.

With falling parachutists while their 'chutes remain unopened, this velocity is believed to be normally within the range of 100 to 150 m.p.h., varying only with altitude, weight, and shape of costume. It is actually quite a comfortable speed for riding on air and the fact of its harmlessness to a human was dramatically demonstrated a quarter of a century ago by a Russian flyer who dropped from a height of 26,575 feet to 650 feet before pulling his rip cord. The sheer fall of five miles took two minutes and twenty seconds

—time long enough for any good surface runner to run considerably more than half a mile.

It requires a maximum of only nine seconds to reach terminal velocity after jumping, during which time you have dropped something over three hundred feet. But it is interesting to reflect that stunt divers have survived jumps off the Golden Gate Bridge at about that height and must have hit the water when falling at very little less than terminal velocity. Which is an indication that it is not necessarily all over for a parachutist whose 'chute does not open when he is over water.

During World War II, I heard of a case of an airman forced to jump from several thousand feet over the ocean without a 'chute, and he successfully withstood the impact and was picked up little the worse for his adventure.

The prize fall of all history, however, must go to British R.A.F. Sergeant Nicholas Stephen Alkemade who was tail gunner in a Lancaster bomber over the Ruhr in Germany one night in March of 1944 when the big plane was hit by enemy fire. A fuel tank exploded, suddenly shooting flaming gasoline down almost the whole length of the fuselage. As he felt the plane heel over out of control, Alkemade reached for his 'chute which he had left hanging on a rack. He was horrified to find it a mass of fire. What could he do? The 'chute was obviously too far gone to be usable even if he could smother the rising flames. His boots were already beginning to burn. He decided to jump anyway, preferring sudden death on the ground to being roasted alive in the sky. This is it, he thought as he yanked open a sizzling hot door and dove into black space 18,000 feet from the ground—three and a half miles straight up!

That's all he could remember until he awoke to see a small patch of stars overhead. Was he dead? He turned his head and moved his arms. His head throbbed and his back pained sharply. He felt cold and damp and noticed he was lying in snow and underbrush four feet deep in a dense fir forest. Slowly he moved his legs and raised himself and tried to sit up.

His boots were gone, his flying suit in shreds. He looked up and down incredulously. Large broken branches above his head showed where he had plummeted into the big trees before crashing through at reduced speed to the wonderful mattress of snow where he had rested deep and protected from the wind for three hours!

When he was eventually carried into a village the Nazi soldiers who took him prisoner scoffed at his story. But higher German authorities organized a thorough investigation which resulted in Alkemade's being given a unique certificate, signed by a German colonel, attesting to the fact that he had actually fallen 18,000 feet without a parachute and lived.

11

Trying Out the Pinions of Man

WE ON THE FLIGHT DECK have become so accustomed to the vibration of four engines that it almost cancels out in the brain. Sometimes I can imagine we are aboard a giant glider coasting effortlessly across the unknown world of night—pioneers of future flight that has not yet wholly unleashed itself from the fetter of earthbound ideas.

Perhaps there comes then an inkling of how Otto Lilienthal must have felt as he studied birds with German thoroughness in the 1870's and '80's and tried with great persistence to translate their secrets into human science. Leonardo long before had designed a flying machine with wings fitted to stirrups and pulleys so that they could be rowed like oars, and in the nineteenth century a whole series of attempts was made to unlock the secret of flight—from Sir George Cayley's propellers to Henson's 25-horsepower steam plane in the 1840's which could not get off the ground.

Lilienthal at first had tried sticks of palisander wood as pinions for his ten-foot wings, the barbs on these "quills" being large goose primaries sewn on tape and fastened to the sticks. He had figured a man of 160 pounds would need wings twenty feet in total span. But a few minutes of diligent but ineffective flapping convinced him that he would also need pectoral muscles correspondingly large: somewhere around four feet thick on his chest. All too clearly statues and paintings of dainty angels flitting aloft bore no relation to the problem of human flight under conditions of earthly gravity.

So Lilienthal tried a different approach. He shifted his attention to soaring birds and built gliders with rigid wings and hawklike tails, and he actually got off the ground in them—gliding downhill into the wind, sometimes for many seconds before his feet touched again.

All during the eighteen-eighties and in the nineties he kept at it, experimenting, methodically trying out wings of different aspect ratios and cambers and shapes. He wrote tables of pressures and got out a book: *Bird Flight as the Basis of the Art of Flying*. He steered by shifting his weight, sliding to right and left on the frame. In all he made more than two thousand glides in safety (evidently few longer than about twenty seconds) until one windy day, August, 19, 1896, a sudden gust flipped his glider over, sending it into a sideways dive out of control. When they picked him up, forty-nine-year-old Otto Lilienthal was breathing his last and just managed to gasp out in stiff German syllables: "Sacrifices must be paid for."

Among all the men who shared the dream of flight it would have been difficult in the year 1900 for the most discerning scholar to have foretold what sort of inventor would be the first actually to penetrate the secret of the birds, to crack the ancient mystery wide open beyond any doubt. Certainly there was nothing to attract particular attention to two bicycle mechanics in Dayton, Ohio, named Wilbur and Orville Wright. Aged thirty-three and twenty-nine years respectively, they were the youngest sons of Bishop Milton Wright of the United Brethren Church.

It is true that both boys had a good deal of mechanical aptitude. They had built a calculating machine that could multiply as well as add, a home telegraph, a typewriter "more simplified than any in existence," hundreds of bicycles including the popular "Wright Special" for $18 retail, the first "balloon tires," and a printing press made with a buggy top mounted on a gravestone which got them into the newspaper business as a means of keeping the press from lying idle.

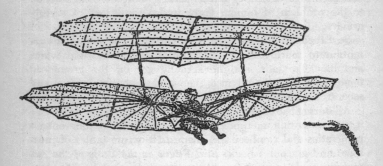

But such examples of ingenuity were not rare in a pioneering nation, especially in the exciting new age of bicycles on tires, of express trains and ocean liners, of horseless carriages—yes, and gliding machines. God alone knew what wonder might be coming next. Anything could happen, and often did—such as the bishop's arrival home one afternoon with a toy flying machine that buzzed to the ceiling. Invented by an ingenious Frenchman named Alphonse Penaud, who originated the elastic-band motor, this double-propelled helicopter immediately fired the imagination of the young Wrights. They wasted no time in putting together a number of model planes and after the death of their hero, Otto Lilienthal, at last tackled the question of why wasn't there some better way to keep a glider on an even keel than having the pilot slide his body back and forth?

With a wonderful mixture of caution and boldness they built first an experimental five-foot kite to try out Wilbur's idea of warpable wings, the ancestor of ailerons. Then, making a pilgrimage to the wind at Kitty Hawk, North Carolina, on the basis of the Weather Bureau's figures of an average velocity of fifteen miles an hour there year in year out, they constructed their first "man-carrying" glider. It weighed just fifty-two pounds and cost fifteen dollars, mostly for spruce spars, ash ribs, and sixty yards of white French sateen cotton sewn to dimensions on sister Katherine's sewing machine.

Though the mosquitoes rose out of the marsh grass on hot still nights so thick that the boys more than once thought of packing up for home and the wind was maddeningly fickle, one day a gale, the next three a doldrum, they somehow never quite quit. A mark of their collectively independent genius was their homemade box of wind, an eighteen-inch starch box fitted with a glass top that became what was probably the first wind tunnel in history and which showed them for the first time that the vacuum above a wing is at least as important as the pressure below in generating the lift essential to flight.

The story of their patient efforts and quiet success with a home-made twin-propellered plane in December 1903 is now too familiar to need repeating—even though it was so astounding at the time that almost no one believed it for several years.

As the twentieth century went into its second decade many new names sprang up in aviation—Farman, Blériot, Paulhan, Ferber, Curtiss, Esnault-Peltrie, Delagrange—and the world was wrenching itself out of its ruts trying to adjust to the wing and the propeller and all their ramifications in speed, distance, and dimension.

Blériot had flown the English Channel in 1909. The next year Paulhan made an altitude record of 4150 feet over Los Angeles and won the *Daily Mail* prize of £10,000 by flying from London to Manchester. In 1911 a prize of $50,000 was offered the winner of an air race across America, coast to coast, an idea so bold that even Orville Wright was moved to remark: "They are attempting the impossible. The machine has not been made that can do it."

Yet it was quickly demonstrated that Orville did not know the wonder of his own works. The trans-America race was won by Calbraith Rodgers who had learned how at the

Wright School in Dayton, soloing after only ninety minutes of instruction. It was said he judged the smoothness of a landing by whether or not it knocked the ashes off his cigar.

The appearance of the several planes that showed up for the start was not much different from the Kitty Hawk original: bi-planes with guy wires all over them, twin-driven propellers, warping cords that had to be worked with the shoulders, ski skids out front and bike wheels beneath. The actual flying time of Rodgers' plane, the *Vin Fiz*, was three days and ten hours between New York and Pasadena, but this was spread over a period of forty-nine days and sixty-nine different landing places as Rodgers fought his way westward, spending six times as many hours repairing his machine as flying it. The whole plane was literally rebuilt four times during the race and the only original parts of it that got to California were its vertical rudder and its drip pan.

A sample Rodgers' problem was his battle with a big eagle that chased the *Vin Fiz* for twenty miles near Waco, Texas, diving at it again and again, clawing the rudder and breaking several wires. To Rodgers it seemed a case of jealous rivalry between the old king of the air and a younger, bigger

challenger—a kind of mad defense in desperation like the Indian attacks on the invading wagon trains that had so recently ended on the ground below.

Teaching mankind the true nature of flying was to be a long process, often exciting, often tedious, sometimes painful. It was to be done by men who tinkered with engines all night in cold barns, by visionaries in cow pastures, by army and navy volunteers, preparing for the unimaginable sky battles of World War I.

By the nineteen-twenties and -thirties lots of mere passengers in the new airliners had come to feel safer when flying fast than slow, to sleep better high than low—both symptoms of a conditioned instinct that was unknown among humanity before the airplane. Yet, strange but true, by now almost half the population has flown enough to gain confidence in the slippery, wallowy air, recognizing it as not just a nothing but a real something with mass and muscle to hold you up—realizing that a wing is more than a beautiful example of streamlining, in fact that it is a deflector that pushes and pulls air downward.

The difference between a passenger today and thirty years ago is striking. Ruth Elder and Amelia Earhart became world figures by flying the Atlantic as passengers, yet now ten thousand passengers may cross it in a day in hundreds of airliners without even patting each other mentally on the back. The change has come because ocean flying suddenly shifted during World War II from something apparently hazardous to the safest kind of flying there is—as proven by the fact that there have been extremely few accidents on the high seas and statistically a lot less than upon any other part of the earth.

How come? The big new airports are what did it. The finances of war built long runways in many places on the coasts of the world's oceans, and on the strategic islands, making it possible for the first time for land planes to take off with really heavy cargoes of payload and fuel. Without big loads ocean flying obviously could not be either profitable or safe. But wheels could lift off much more weight than seaplane hulls which are held back by the buffeting friction of waves—so that boat-bottomed clippers had to go, even though they had been the first ocean airliners. It was a change as practical as it was paradoxical and it altered the world's thinking overnight.

The decision to use four engines was another factor in trimming the seas to present size. Why not two, or three, or five motors on ocean spanning planes? Or six? Why four?

The answer: four is just many enough for safety, just few enough for economy. Fact is: engines sometimes quit. Wolfgang Langewiesche, the test pilot and expositor extraordinary of flying, has analyzed it clearly. He says "the odds that a single engine will get you across the Atlantic are about 500 to 1." This was good enough for Lindbergh but if the airlines had no better a batting average they would be losing a ship to the drink every couple of days.

Two engines are a big improvement, says Langewiesche. "The chance that two independent engines should happen to quit in the same hour is 1:25,000,000." Since a good twin-motored plane is able to fly on either engine alone, a million average flying days would see it forced down only once with dead engines. That bet sold the DC–3 to the domestic airlines and has kept them in business ever since. When you are flying over land, even a forced landing is not so serious with the nearest airport at most forty-five minutes away (by law) when the first engine stops, still nearer should the second quit, and downhill all the way.

But over the ocean where there are no landing places two engines just aren't enough. Forty-five minutes is one thing; four or five hours another. The trouble is, explains Langewiesche, two engines in the same airplane can't be wholly independent. Not only may the same flaw be in the second engine, which probably has a fairly similar history, but when the first one dies it literally tosses its burden to the second, heaping this on top of the load already there, regardless. This means the plane is forced to limp, fly slightly sideways, increase drag, slow down. As the lone laboring engine gets hot and you open its cowl flaps the drag gets worse, the speed still slower, fuel consumption higher, strain greater, new breakdowns more likely.

Four engines are the least that can really do the job—and they do it so well that there is no percentage in spending money on more. It has been calculated that each engine quits about once in 6000 hours on the average. And when that happens the other three engines can carry on without any appreciable difference—except in the minds of those aboard. In fact any two engines can drag you home in a pinch.

About the most startling thing that can happen in a four-motored plane is to have all four motors stop at once. That has happened twice in my own experience—but fortunately forced landings were avoided both times. The four engines are virtually independent of each other, outside of fuel supply and the pilot's mind—and sure enough both these factors were responsible on each occasion. We were not totally out of gas but one of the pilots had left a valve closed in the feed line by mistake, until the sudden sputter of four engines followed by deathly silence woke him in a hurry! Though I was busy checking our position for the S O S each time of whining, crescendoed descent, I'll never forget the expression of quiet horror on the pilots' faces.

Despite such nerve-straining episodes, any well-tried four-engined airplane is safe for ocean flying. Without hesitation I'll bet my life it will fly as long as the engines get their fuel. A legion of men have been betting their lives on this every day since World War II and who can think of anyone who lost his bet? One cannot deny that it may happen someday—but so may you be hit by a meteorite.

Another fascinating problem analyzed by Langewiesche is the old "engineering curse" that they used to say limited the airplane's range, sort of naturally, to about 750 miles. This was all too true for any size of airplane. It would take about two thirds of the total lift to hold the plane up in the air. Of the final third, at least half would have to be fuel—say four or five hours worth—leaving the remainder for payload which was the real reason for flying. That last sixth quite literally had to pay for everything, being as vital to the airplane as a pack to a pack horse. If you wanted to fly more than 1000 miles you could do it of course, as did Lindbergh, but you would have to give up payload for fuel. From the viewpoint of an airline stockholder you might as well go back to wearing snowshoes.

What then was the solution? Size of plane? No. Bigger airplanes need bigger fuel tanks and bigger, beefier engines —almost in proportion—and longer runways.

Lightness? No. Lightness reduces strength.

Power? Speed? No. Fuel consumption rises proportionately. You can't get along with an economy-size engine built just for long range either, because it wouldn't have enough power to clear the trees on take-off. Like the pelican, the airplane just doesn't have much margin in getting off the ground.

The answer turned out to be streamlining. Of course the rudimentary streamlining was done in the first couple of decades of flying: eliminating struts, cowling the engine, retracting the landing gear. But the airplane even in its DC–3 heyday was still a rough diamond with protruding rivets and airscoops and angular windshields and humpy fuselage. Polishing that stuff into a slick article made all the difference at 200 m.p.h. and upwards. The ultimate in streamlining efficiency is probably the flying wing at moderate speeds and the rocket at high speeds. The sureness of their coming can be measured in the benefits already gained, in the fact that it takes less than a quarter as much propeller or jet thrust, pound for pound, to pull a modern sky liner through the air as it did to pull a strut and wire biplane in 1920. Did you know that by just smoothing out the DC–3-type riveted skin the designers added four paying passengers to each Atlantic crossing?

Thus the engineering curse is solved by smoothness, by a purer slipperiness that lets the airplane slide ahead faster through the sticky air, lets each pound of fuel drive it farther, leaves more room for payload, stretches the range two or three fold.

Harder than the engineering curse to solve have been the hazards of mechanical complexity and traffic density as airplanes grew in size and number. Before the age of jets, for example, the fastest things moving on an airplane were its propellers. Propellers therefore have invited trouble more than the slower parts. Sometimes also this source of danger is so remote from its consequences that diagnosis is difficult. Thus when a Florida-bound airliner in 1948 was suddenly shaken by a loud bang at 22,000 feet, followed by severe vibration and depressurization of the cabin, no one knew just what was the matter—not even after a pilot noticed that parts of the No. 3 engine were dropping off and its propeller already gone. Only minutes later was it discovered that a purser had been killed in the galley by a propeller blade that had knifed through the fuselage, letting the sealed air escape.

Another time as a DC–4 approached a landing field in Michigan a similar noise was heard, followed by violent shaking. Then a pilot discovered a fire in his No. 1 engine and saw that both No. 1 and No. 2 propellers had disappeared. Only careful investigation later on the ground revealed that some mysterious internal breakage in the No. 2 engine had made its crankshaft lock, shearing off its propeller which flew into the No. 1 propeller, breaking that in turn and sending it hurtling through the edge of the left wing.

Such tendencies of propellers, even if rare, have disturbed dreams of more than one crew member trying to sleep in flight. Some of us have gone so far as to wonder: could it be for the very purpose of reducing our temptation to snooze that the C–54's bunks have been located exactly where a thrown blade could slice a sleeper in two?

When reversible-pitch propellers became common after World War II another danger appeared: if a propeller should inadvertently become reversed in flight the airplane is apt to be thrown out of control, a typical instance being the Martin 202 which suffered this very mishap over Minnesota in 1950 and spun downward turning to the right until its right wing hit the ground, cartwheeling it violently and killing all aboard.

Collisions between airplanes are about as common as collisions between ships at sea, despite the airplane's advantage of an extra dimension to dodge in. But air collisions have proved definitely the more disastrous for obvious reasons. Even the airlines, flying their different courses at carefully assigned separate altitudes, have their collisions—most often near airports where congestion is greatest, where climbing and descending planes must somewhere pass each other in altitude.

The collision a few years ago between two C–54 airliners over the Oakland range station is a fair example. Both planes were heading approximately eastward and therefore could legally use the same "odd thousand" feet of altitude as they crossed the range. Somehow the Oakland tower failed to inform them of each other's presence, and again the improbable happened as they hit blindly at 3000 feet directly above the station, one slicing off the entire tail section of the other, sending the remainder spinning downwards out of control to crash on a highway, involving also a truck and two cars which were unable to duck the flaming debris.

One might think that anyone unlucky enough to be in the

tail of a plane cut in two by collision would have no chance without a parachute, but I heard of a tail gunner who proved otherwise in World War II. What appeared to this unsuspecting fellow as rather prolonged evasive action by his pilot during a sky battle was eventually revealed to his consciousness as the natural "falling leaf" gyrations of his tail assembly after the rest of the bomber had flown on for several minutes without it. Yet the wild tail turned out to have some fair gliding qualities of its own and actually made a passable crash landing in a forest that left the gunner more amazed than hurt.

Less blest was an airliner full of Delta Airline company officials that was just landing at Muscogee Airport in Georgia when a private plane also landed unseen squarely on top of it. The airliner was still a few feet off the ground and, feeling his tail being forced down, its pilot applied his throttle and zoomed upward again to about 150 feet, dragging the smaller plane along like a dragonfly its mate—whereupon both stalled, and crashed to the ground, killing all occupants.

Collisions with birds for some strange reason are getting less frequent in spite of the fact that airplanes are becoming faster and more numerous. Perhaps the feathered flyers are getting better adapted to the competition begun at Kitty Hawk, for although they used to wreck more than an airplane a year and actually killed several of their big rivals, mostly by flying straight through windshields into the pilot's faces, the Civil Aeronautics Board recorded only three bird collisions in the decade after World War II (involving a buzzard, a small duck, and a pair of seagulls) none of which injured anyone or wrecked an airplane.

Collisions with electric wires occur fairly often and airplanes usually survive them, but the collision record is not so good with trees—still worse with solid ground. However, there have been cases when an airplane hit a mountain hard enough to bend propeller blades and damage landing gear and yet bounced back into the air to arrive safely at its destination.

I could go on and on with case histories of air accidents. Their causes range all the way from playfulness to panic with the biggest factor usually just human carelessness or poor judgment—often fatigue and boredom contributing.

Of course there are lots of warning lights, bells, horns and other devices in modern airplanes to remind the pilots when fuel is dangerously low, airspeed too slow, wheels not locked down for landing, a door not properly shut . . . But still the main reliance is inevitably on human alertness to avoid trouble. Anyway there is a limit to how many gadgets you can cram into a cockpit and leave peace of mind enough to fly.

It hardly needs repeating that the littlest things often make the biggest difference in flying—even the interpretation of a gesture or a phrase in conversation between crew mates of long acquaintance. One recent accident was traced to a pilot's pointing to the landing gear lights which the co-pilot unthinkingly took to be an order to raise the gear—in this case too soon. In another accident at the pilot's command, "Pull 'em up!" the co-pilot had raised the flaps instead of the intended landing wheels.

The very real problems of the modern pilot can hardly be appreciated without seeing him at work, without studying the basic instruments in the mechanical, electrical jungle that is the cockpit. The number of dials and handles and buttons that must be within his reach has grown so large that for twenty years and more they have covered not only all the walls, the ceiling, and most of the floor but special hummocks of them rise up from his feet, irregular boxes and levers, not to overlook that weird growth called the pedestal between the pilots' seats which contains so many throttle and other control knobs that it looks like a Christmas tree, each series of handles a different color to aid the pilot (who has been checked for color blindness) as he darts his fingers this way and that as if to pluck grapes in an overgrown vineyard.

Seeing the crew preparing for take-off in any modern airliner is akin to witnessing a symphony orchestra tuning up for a concert. Each man has his check list of so many vital items that he couldn't possibly trust his memory alone—and the pilot's check list normally contains between thirty and a hundred. First there is the "Before Starting Engines" list: check (1) drift meter "caged," (2) landing gear lever "full down" and "latched," (3) landing gear up-latch lever "unlatched, (4) emergency landing gear extension lever to "up" (open), (5) hydraulic pressure (1800 lbs. minimum), (6) emergency brake pressure (1000 lbs. ± 50), (7) automatic pilot hydraulic pressure valve "off," (8) hydraulic hand pump bypass valve "closed," (9) battery switch "cart battery," (10) instrument switch "on," (11) navigation lights "on" (night) "off" (day), (12) wing de-icers "off," (13) propeller anti-icers "off," (14) generators "off," (15) ignition switches "off," (16) pitot heaters "off," (17) . . . and on and on.

And then there are the "Before Take-off" check list, the "After Take-off and During Climb" list, the lists for "Cruising," "Before Landing," "After Landing," and "Securing the Airplane."

Along with all this checking inside the airplane of course there must be a nearly continuous checking outside as well—visually during take-off, landing, and between if conditions permit—otherwise mostly by radio, especially when in congested areas.

Here, for sample, is what a pilot is up against as he approaches Chicago from New York on a busy winter day. The visibility is fair at Chicago but A.T.C. (Air Traffic Control) has stacked up the incoming planes anyway, just to be on the safe side—that is, each has been ordered to circle at a different altitude till its turn to land, each new arrival being added at the top, each clearance to land removing another plane from the bottom, all descending in altitude at the same time, step by step working their way to earth.

Light ice has been reported over Toledo, and there is some radio skip with the usual static. The pilot tries to report over Goshen, 100 miles east of Chicago, using his assigned number: Flight 422. He hears in his earphones: "422 from Chicago clearance. A.T.C. clears 422 to . . . squeal, bzzz-zz . . . 6099 at 4000 . . . squeak . . ." There must be two planes on the same frequency, he thinks. " . . . Stand by 6099 . . . 207 from Detroit clearance. Stand by, Cleveland. Report each thousand feet on descent . . . Stand by, Cleveland. South Bend from 644. Changing over . . . 644 from South Bend. Changing over. South Bend altimeter 2978 squeal . . . Chicago from 311, I can't hold any longer. I'm low on gas. Give me clearance to Joliet or some place. Tell airways . . . squeal, squeal . . . leaving thweee thousand feeee-e bzzzzzzzzzz . . ."

The co-pilot has a try at it. "Chicago from 422," he says. "Stand by 422," replies the radio; "355 from Springfield squeal . . ."

"Best not try to bust in now," says the captain. "311 is in trouble and there'll be more in trouble soon."

"But Cap, we need a clearance. We haven't got any authority to be here."

"Never mind, Bud. Remember the one thing that saved A.T.C. from folding up years ago was that God always packs such a hell of a lot of room into three dimensions."

The radio continues: "Detroit from Chicago, when was 181 over Tecumseh? . . . Chicago from Detroit, over Tecumseh at 44 at 5000 . . . Detroit from Chicago, okay, 44 at 9000 . . . No, no. Five—two, three, four, five . . . Cleveland from 192, cleared at 6000? Thought we were cleared to let down to four. Going back up . . . Stand by 192 . . . no, NO, two, three, four, FIVE . . . well, we're down to five now and . . ."

That's the way it always is when traffic and weather get together. They can put more airplanes into the air easily enough, but more radio channels is another thing. There are just so many frequency bands in existence. Emergencies get little special attention, and guessing is vital to success. Avoidance of collisions around big cities is inevitably left to chance at times.

In this case the pilot had to allow two extra hours for holding over Chicago, plus time for missed approaches. Two hours on instruments in the overcast, blind, always turning, turning . . . After half an hour the pilot was picking his ear and running his fingers through his hair. His eyes were getting tired. He wanted to look up something in the procedure book but decided not to. It was too dark to read without lights, and if you turned up the lights you couldn't see outside—not even after it was dark again—until your eyes had taken time to adjust.

When a hypnotist goes to work on a subject he puts him in a comfortable chair in a darkened room and makes him look steadily at a lighted object while listening to a monotonous musical tone. That's exactly what happens to pilots on instruments. They sit comfortably in the darkened cockpit gazing fixedly at luminous dials, reading quivering needles of light, with all the while the buzzing of the radio range in their ears—a perfect set-up for hypnotic sleep!

Is it any wonder that pilots sometimes forget what beam they are on, take the wrong reciprocals, or start their letdown a half minute too soon? If bad luck should add to this a needle dial that is 30° off, an automatic loop that has taken to telling lies, a leak in the hydraulic system that controls the flaps, landing gear, and brakes, some freezing mist on the windshield, or a burned out landing light—things that happen every day—the preponderance of the factors of disaster can easily develop beyond any practical hope of resistance.

Even as we take necessary measures for safety against these dangers we have to beware safety's own saturation point. We must remember that 3510 pounds of lifesaving devices can become an anchor of death and forty-six flashing red lights, buzzers, horns, bells, and radio traffic signals may ultimately arouse only a craving for paper dolls. Like Pyrrhus, we now hear the captains crying ". . . another such victory and we are lost!"

There is ground for hope of remedying this pilots' dilemma, however, for an organization called the Air Navigation Board has been set up by the United States government charged and authorized to solve the whole complex problem of flight traffic in co-ordination with all similar agencies everywhere. Radio engineers, traffic engineers, and human engineers have long been at work on it, keeping their plans flexible enough to adopt useful future inventions, yet steadfastly progressing toward a basic permanent arrangement that promises to be as simple, foolproof and efficient as is possible to man.

This ultimate common system of air navigation and traffic control is scheduled to include the recently instituted omnirange direction setup which already tells flying crews their exact direction from two or more known range points. But as soon as the new DME (distance-measuring equipment) is in full use only one range point will be essential at a time, for the combined equipment will continuously inform the pilot or navigator exactly how far he is as well as his precise direction from the range, thus effectively pinpointing his position. In addition the plane's altitude and individual identification will be continuously available to the control towers by automatic transponder installed in the plane to reply to radio code queries, just as its exact latitude and longitude position are already available by radar. Thus traffic control officers will be able to check all aircraft in their areas at will, helping lost planes locate themselves in emergencies, directing individual flights through traffic with the simplest of spoken clearances on private frequencies: "proceed," "hold," "go left," "go up," "go down"—keeping a constant flow control to and from runways, spacing the landings at least thirty seconds apart on each strip, allowing the jet liners to take off and climb swiftly to economical jet altitudes while the propeller craft are assigned to the slower-piston stratas in the lower sky.

By that time two-way traffic will not be separated by altitude alone but by horizontal track as well, and perhaps slight separations in track will also divide planes following close upon one another like cars on a six-lane highway. This course precision, now impossible except by impractical visual methods, will become easy when the automatic course line computer is standard equipment in a few years. This is a simple device that makes geometric computations electrically, giving the pilot his exact true course at all times. It must be tuned, however, to the Omni-Range for guidance, hence its delayed appearance pending completion of ground equipment.

To top off the future pilot's composure in traffic he will have before him a maplike screen on which will be projected pips of light representing not only his own position but those of other craft, enabling him to monitor the traffic situation continuously and check navigation by eyesight in the densest cloud. In so-called "blind" landings he will also have the latest refinements of the instrument landing system (ILS) with precision-approach radar (descended from World War II's ground-control approach to supplement ILS if need be) and, should he come out of the overcast before landing, approach lights directing his eyes to the glide path and runway with graduated intersecting beams.

Inside the cockpit the jungle will be more orderly by then too—more standardized, probably simpler, though it will take an expert to realize it. That is the main province of the human engineers: to match up men and machines for optimum practicability. Their work in effect must cut short the slow threshing of evolution which in ages past solved comparable problems for the flying insects, perfected the gyrotronic sense organs of flies (vibrating "haltere" rods behind each wing), the airspeed meters of locusts, the bank indicators of dragonflies, the bees' and birds' system of celestial navigation . . .

Elimination of everything unessential is a big load off the crew's brains. When the flight engineer wants to check whether his battery generators are working he used to have to read a dial needle pointing to numbers of amperes of charge or discharge. In future he will only see a green or red light indicating "yes" or "no." With fifty such indicators shorn of their wool, the crew will be spared much of the dangerous excess information from which they have long had to select, abstract, interpolate, extrapolate, derive, and ignore —sometimes literally to the point of death. The airplane will enter a new phase of progress.

Right now about the most definite thing to be said about the airplane's first half century is that it has grown so amazingly in muscle. It is a fledgling that has already outdistanced our thundering locomotive in horsepower and humbled our dauntless battleship in potency of destruction. Although we have not even completely recovered from the shock of its birth, its adolescent accomplishments are piling up at a rate to confound us.

Did you know that in September 1941 a lone R.A.F. land patrol plane forced a German submarine to surrender near the Hebrides? And the same year an R.A.F. fighter pilot in a Hurricane, having run out of ammunition, defeated a German Messerschmitt by ramming it, using his wing to knock off the enemy's elevator and send him spinning into the English Channel.

An American DC3 pilot once faced an entirely different situation when trapped while flying through an Alaskan canyon by a wind so strong he could not make any headway against it, so he "just throttled the old girl down" and flew out backwards. And there is the astonishing but well-authenticated case in 1956 of the U.S.A.F. jet fighter pilot who shot himself down by diving ahead of a volley he had just fired, only to be overtaken and riddled by his own bullets as he attempted to level off.

Probably the most amazing single feat of all yet accomplished in human flying—and one that not only should have aroused the envy of the birds but is well worth telling in some detail—is the jet rescue of a blacked-out flyer in the Korean War in 1951 by two other airplanes literally using their wings as crutches to help him home. It happened on November 16 to Captain John Paladino of North Little Rock, Arkansas, who was roaring back at 500 m.p.h. in his single-place Republic F-84 from a raid on North Korean railroads inside MIG Alley. Luckily for him he had two good friends flying in the same formation at 32,000 feet when suddenly his oxygen supply failed and he faded into unconsciousness.

"I was flight leader that day," recalled Paladino, talking to correspondents afterwards, "and we were returning from a routine job. There was another flight of eighty-fours on their way home ahead of us, so I started to lead mine out of the way. You never know it when you're not getting enough oxygen; in fact you feel wonderful—sort of rocked, like on vodka. Your co-ordination and reasoning are off a little, but you feel right up to par. That's how I felt, until it was too late to do anything about it. The first I knew I was in trouble was when I lost my vision. The instruments went hazy and I couldn't see the flight ahead of us. That's all I remember."

"I saw John turn," said Captain Jack Miller, his wing man, picking up the story, "and I figured he was going to make a regular three-sixty turn to let the other boys get ahead. But he only got through about ninety degrees when he suddenly went into a steep dive to the left. I thought maybe he was practicing evasive action or something. After he'd gone down a few thousand feet his plane did a 'pitch-up.' That means it went through the speed of sound and then, because of a characteristic of the plane, suddenly nosed up into a climb. I still thought he was just fooling around. Then he fell off into another steep dive, this time to the right. He did another pitch-up and went into another climb. After he had climbed a few thousand feet he stalled again, only this time he straightened out on a level course at about thirty thousand. I noticed that he was a few degrees off course, but I still thought he was okay."

"I radioed Paladino," said Lieutenant Wood McArthur, his other wing man, who by now suspected something was wrong. "I said, 'Fox Leader, this is Fox Two. Are you all right?' And he answered, 'Yes, I'm okay.' He sounded quite normal and his plane was leveling off all right. I caught up with him and noticed he was tugging at his oxygen mask. I told him to throttle back for the descent home. He didn't do it, so I radioed him again and this time he slowed down."

"I pulled alongside too," said Miller, "and we went along like that for a while. Then I noticed that John's head was resting against the canopy. Then all of a sudden he slumped forward. We knew right away what was wrong. I radioed him, 'Fox Leader, Fox Three. Are you all right?' He didn't answer and I called Fox Two (McArthur) and told him I thought Johnny had passed out. I told Woody to pull up in front of him and try to shake him awake with the blast from his tail. Woody started to. Then we decided that might send Johnny into a bad spin, so we pulled back. 'Woody,' I said, 'put your wing under his wing and I'll put mine under his other wing and we'll keep him level until he comes to.' Just as we got into position John fell off into a steep left turn towards Woody so I radioed Woody to catch him. 'Roger, I got him,' he said. Woody pushed him a little too hard and he rolled over onto me. We did that twice. The second time was not as bad as the first and he began to straighten out."

While making these difficult maneuvers of "catching" their fallen comrade of course neither Miller's nor McArthur's wing actually touched Paladino's wing. It was the stiff cushions of air flowing over the wing tips at 400 m.p.h. that actually supported Paladino, just as the cushions of air inside parachute canopies support parachutists drifting down the sky. "If John had been conscious and had exerted all his strength to keep his plane level," explained Miller, "I could probably have banged my wing against his, but it would have taken all my strength on the stick to break through the air flowing around his wing."

From then on all Miller and McArthur had to do was use their flying skill to keep their wings under Paladino's, carefully guiding his plane downward toward breathable air, making sure he didn't fall into a spin which might let him crash before he could regain consciousness. When they got to 15,000 feet the two wing men could see Paladino's head nodding and they both radioed to him: "Wake up, Johnny! Wake up, wake up! Hey, Johnny!"

Paladino did not answer but soon Miller saw him tilt his head back and he told him to switch his oxygen feed to 100 per cent. Paladino could not remember it afterward but in his half consciousness he responded enough to twist the valve part way. Then at 13,500 feet his eyes opened and he snapped awake. He was breathing fairly dense air now besides what little extra oxygen his apparatus supplied.

After he landed Paladino's face was a deep purple and he had a fierce headache, but he was happy to be alive after his 100-mile 15 minute ride through the valley of the shadow at better than half the speed of sound—snatched from Icarus by a maneuver unprecedented in the history of flight!

12

Music in the Air

As I FLY I can't help but hear the sky moving around me—around the airplane. We all hear it subconsciously most of the time, that enduring moan just audible beneath the engine's roar. Akin to the lower ocean's thunder of rushing foam, the sky's tongue is a volatile organ of its own, a characteristic voice that inflects with each rising wrinkle of wind, each purling fold of air.

There are words to the song too, words to the wise who understand them—words of joy and the feel of the air, informative words about the eddies you cannot see, about airspeed and air density—stern words warning of the death that lurks below.

The place where sky music gets strongest of all is at velocities near and above the speed of sound. This is because of the nature of sound itself, of air compressibility. It is a clue as to why the flight pioneers had such trouble in passing the

194

"sound barrier" in speed—even as to why they considered it a barrier.

Sound of course is nothing more than waves of pressure created by vibration or shock. These waves do not move like ripples traveling the length of a loose rope, perpendicularly (lengthwise) to the (sideways) motion of the rope. Instead they move parallel or in the same direction as the motion of the medium they are in: toward and away from their own source. In other words particles of air transmitting sound vibrate in parallel waves of alternating supernormal and subnormal pressure.

These waves in fact *are* the sound. And they travel not only through air but through any substance—and the solider the faster. They move at four miles a second through the hard steel of a railroad track, at slightly less than a mile a second through the softer medium of water, at only about 1100 feet per second through the extreme softness of air. They are a milder form of the shock waves caused by explosion blasts and move at the same speed.

To understand this mysterious, almost hypothetical, barrier that tried the wits and courage of thousands of pioneers for the best part of a decade, we must visualize what is going on upstream from a wing as well as downstream and all around, especially the faint but definite waves of pressure and suction that are continuously advancing ahead of it in the sky, probing forward like long-range ethereal whiskers to enable the air to feel the wing's approach and start flowing into its pattern before the wing itself arrives.

This invisible run-ahead of pressure impulses in front of the airplane is akin to the shaping of swells to windward of an island and it occurs with the speed of sound: 760 m.p.h. in average sea-level air. In slow planes it naturally extends far ahead—at least as many miles ahead as you can hear the airplane coming. The sky is thus preparing itself, shaping its molecules to accept the approaching wing long before it can be certain it will ever get there. In faster planes flying around 500 to 600 m.p.h. the run-ahead extends only a little way forward because the airplane is almost keeping up with its sound and the relative run-ahead speed is only the difference between the speeds of sound and of the airplane.

But when an airplane has stepped up its speed to mach 1, the varying actual speed of sound, the run-ahead ceases entirely and the air-flow pattern of pressures changes so radically that the very principles of wing lift are altered. What was a smooth efficient wing becomes in effect a crude club that has no lift and stalls in the sky. Its bow wave of air, unable to outspeed the airplane that now equals it in velocity, can no longer escape to disperse its energy but is locked against the machine streaking across the heavens while its pressure builds up with terrifying rapidity, sending the subsonic-type unprepared wing into a convulsion of vibration that usually either breaks it apart or stalls the whole airplane earthward out of control. This phenomenon of explosive compressibility of air is called a shock wave and is virtually the same thing as the initial outward air blast from an exploding bomb! Riding such a power wave and even prodding it into greater pressures is what in effect the sonic airplane does—therein building its own dilemma by ramming virgin air that has not felt its approach nor had time to shape itself to facilitate its passage. If the speeds of plane and sound are indeed exactly balanced the shock wave can amazingly stand stationary upon the wing—invisible, unimaginable, a still photograph of shock blast in material form through which air is continuously flowing at 700-odd miles an hour, yet the pressure of which may be 15 pounds per square inch at one spot and only 5 pounds less than an inch away.

PROGRESSIVE SOUND-SHOCK WAVES

You have heard of the daring test pilots who cracked this sonic barrier and ultimately conquered it. They did it not in one grand swoop but by a long, deliberate process like a chick pecking stubbornly at the inside of an egg until, after gradually weakening it, the shell falls apart to reveal a new world.

Those who first touched the crux of the problem probably were just a little too full of beans for their better judgment. Perhaps they had to be. Test Pilot Langewiesche has described his conception of the first nearly supersonic dive. A young fighter pilot seven miles high one day doing close to 400 m.p.h. with no urgent business decided to try the thrill of a high-speed dive. So he winged over, aimed his nose straight down and opened her up wide, feeling the tingling wonder of speed unreined, the crescendo of the scale: 450 . . . 500 . . . 550 . . . 600 . . .

Since airplanes are made for stability, this one tended to lift its nose again, to come back to level flight and reduce its excess speed, but the pilot firmly held the stick forward enforcing his will like a cow puncher breaking a broom-tail bronc. Soon he thought he was going faster than any man ever had who lived to tell it—and probably he was. The idea might have been useful as a hint. Could he hold on any longer? Should he? Before he had time to decide, the winged bronco went strangely tame under his hand. With a shudder and a buck the plane ceased resisting his pressure on the stick and became ominously *willing* to dive. Its roar dwindled into a soft, mushy sound and its nose was sucked downward as if in a maelstrom. The invisible pattern of pressures around it had changed from the known into the unknown.

Apprehensive, the pilot pulled back on the stick to start leveling off—but the ship did not answer. It was as if the elevators were slapping impotently in a vacuum. By then the plane was plunging a mile every five seconds, and as the horrified young man still tugged frantically at his stick the machine screamed into a hillside like a bullet—and exploded in a high white flame.

Runaway dives of this sort happened every now and then in the early nineteen-forties and no one knew just what had gone wrong. Sometimes the planes spun or wobbled or skipped like a stone on a pond. People on the earth sometimes said the tail must have broken or the pilot had had one too many. But in a few cases the pilot was able to describe the awful nose heaviness and the berserk controls over his radio just before he crashed. Many scraps of real evidence were thus collected, carefully preserved and examined.

By the end of World War II it was widely recognized that new aircraft designs would be necessary to cope with speeds approaching the sonic wall and tests would have to be made to supply data for the designers. Tremendous supersonic wind tunnels were speedily engineered and built. Then, as the designers worked out each new experimental high-speed model—often by art as much as science—the test pilots tried them out, actually proved them in the sky.

It is hard to imagine a more soul-straining project or to think of another occasion short of war when dozens of highly trained pilots have given their lives in a cause as hazardous and significant. Once each man reached 700-odd m.p.h. and lost control he had no chance. The powerful slipstream pressures at that velocity made it out of the question for him to think of bailing out.

Yet the sacrifice in human lives and the millions of dollars spent recording and analyzing and testing the facts inevitably bore fruit for the rest of humanity. Month by month the tabulated records of strain gauges and photo-recorders pieced together a vision of a new world of speed. Several test pilots who saw white fog over their wings while pulling out of dives at more than 600 m.p.h. revealed that the passing sky is forced to expand so sharply around mach .8 that even normal, warm, dry air can be refrigerated into condensation—a new version of the vapor trail. Puzzled engineers had to allow for the fact that when the airplane as a whole is flying just below mach 1. parts of its slipstream (usually just above the wing) are already going faster than mach 1. They remembered of course that for a similar discrepancy the whole development of high-speed flying had had to await perfection of the jet engine: because spinning propellers, inevitably moving faster than the wing behind them, were always being nullified by their own sonic barrier of compressibility before they could pull the airplane itself even nearly that fast.

When you hear the familiar yowl of a propellered airliner taking off you hear indeed the sonic wall being nudged by its propeller tips whirling close to mach 1. A million windowpanes being scored by glass cutters in unison is what it sounds like. And it means that the air just doesn't have the resilience to get out of the way in time. It demonstrates that the propeller tips have topped their limit of effectiveness, that any increase in r.p.m. will not add to their pulling power, may even reduce it with distorted pressures as when its shape has been altered by a coat of ice.

No doubt it was such new-learned behavior of the propeller slipstream that brought out the modern square-cut windmill blade—and earthbound developments like General Electric's slicing machine that revolves at 65,000 r.p.m.! The rim of this circular blade purposefully moves faster than sound to form a cutting edge of compressed air so sharp that it slices hard metals into sheets two millionths of an inch thick —yet the blade itself never gets dull for only the air edge that it keeps recreating touches the work and that edge has diamondlike teethlets of unimaginable thinness that are in reality supersonic jet streams of invisible air molecules.

For passenger transport supersonic planes will obviously have to increase in size, and the problem of what large shape will best avoid excessive turbulence at their speeds is pointing toward the full-scale fin-winged rocket as an optimum vehicle above mach 2. But what of mach 5, mach 10? Time will be the pudding.

Certainly our present intensive research is widening in that direction, taking on an amazing scope. New alloys are being tested for heat "creep," the tendency for metal to soften and stretch as friction raises skin temperatures into the hundreds of degrees; and for speed "flutter," a destructive vibration likely to start somewhere around mach 2; and for resistance to raindrops which become bullets at supersonic speeds. Guided missiles already are navigating by radar, and by gyro and other delicate inertial systems, even by mechanized celestial observation. Their fins with razor-thin diamond-shaped cross-sections steer, roll, or lift them just as if they were airplanes. Some have ram-jet motors for thin-air stratospheric travel. Some have futuristic rocket motors for vacuous ionospheric routes.

These "birds" (as missile men call them) take off with an indescribable sound that is the combination of a bone-shaking roar and the scream of a thousand angry eagles. Even higher in pitch is the accompanying ultrasonic vibration that, witnesses say, seems to press directly upon the brain, bypassing the ears entirely.

Once they are off, the birds are out of sight in a blinding flash and must be followed by telescope, telecamera, radar, radio, television . . . Most fascinating to me of these automatic reports is the audible tone that is recorded on magnetic tape as broadcast from the missile's instruments: an eerie kind of symphony in which altimeters, thermometers, airspeed indicators, cosmic-ray counters, all express themselves musically together. First you hear the quiet harmony of the bird at rest on its launching platform, the tones, deep and shrill, of its continuous-reporting instruments, like skirling bagpipes. And mingled in this drone the intermittent-reporting instruments: the tinkling cosmic glockenspiels, the magnetic harps.

When the missile is fired of course the music changes. The cello thermometers bow up the scale as combustion heat rises. The bassoons of pressure grow more insistent. The tinkling melody is joined by the strained dissonances of the control fins struggling to keep the bird aimed straight. Overall vibration is heard as a guttural growl, rhythmic rolling of the missile a recurrent groan.

It is only when the slender craft has risen free of the earth's atmosphere that the discords fade. In the vacuum of space there is no air to roll it, no external vibration at all. The fins completely relax in nothingness. The bird's song changes from minor to major harmony, exulting in its new freedom, singing among the asteroids.

13

Magnetism of the Sphere

As I MUSE upon the cloud plains beneath my starboard wing and see the halo of the moon, and the glow of St. Elmo's fire on our propellers, I think of the minds of other mortals near me who are witness to these sights. What does Pilot Blake Cloud see in the salmon dawn? Does our engineer from Texas reckon the source of thunder? Will radioman Ernie Silvers wonder at the birth of snow?

Even the greatest minds, in describing what they see of mystery in the world, have confessed the feeble power of their human comprehension before it, attempting only the beginning of awareness of the all.

To see what they see, one can try virtually any corner of nature's estate. And vision will not be limited by what is looked at so much as by the mind behind the eye that sees it. With my mind's eye therefore I testify to the mystery of the world: a shooting star, a girl before her mirror, an old clock's story, the passing of a cloud, the weight of gold on the balance wheel of commerce. The eye is verily more critical than what it looks upon. For what avails it to sweep the sky or wash the window if the eye be not clean?

I know the aspect of the mystery is not really greater in air than in water or land or fire, but somehow the contrasts with time and things of the day's work pluck my life strings more sweetly in air.

I am writing of the world of free air and freer thoughts—of the ocean that has a bottom but no top—of the wind's way and the cloud's way and the way of the bird and the shrouded night—of the sound wave and the light wave and the howl of vibrant electronics turned to the unearthly note of the cat's soul, the magnetic pole.

Cats have an affinity for magnetism, I hear, and they are certainly a tradition as generators of static electricity. I have a feeling too that thunderstorms disturb them emotionally because of their feline sensitivity to the pull of Faraday's magnetic lines of force. Which may explain also why they feel so surely the potentiality for lightning building up in their vicinity, enabling them in some reported cases to escape to a more neutral spot before the fatal strike.

Could there be a further and less understood connection between magnetism and the mind as examplified in the telepathy of cats, and in the geomagnetic field which pervades our entire world with the evident fullness of a universal mind? All too clearly his individual subconsciousness may allow a man to be afraid of all cats simply because he was startled one night thirty years ago by a particular cat which has now been dead for a quarter of a century.

Pondering these things, I check my navigation instruments once more and write down the corrected facts in my log. "Time: 02:46. True airspeed: 194 kts. Average ground-speed: 180 kts. Temperature: +4°. Altitude: 11,000. Course: 92°. Wind: 160° at 25 kts. Compass heading: 120°. Magnetic variation: 20° W. Magnetic deviation 2° E."

We are now about an hour off the coast of Ireland, and I think of Donegal Bay, the gray rocks of Achill and the brown bogs and patchy green fields beyond, where I once lived for a month in a family of sixteen children in Swinford, County Mayo. Perhaps I can feel faintly the geomagnetic favor of Connemara's stones. At any rate it will be good to be over land again, and I am glad we have our reserve fuel in view of what we wasted in the unforeseen affair of the ice.

"How about a radio bearing?" I ask Ernie Silvers sitting next to me. "I have no stars and we've been on dead reckoning for nearly four hundred miles now. We need a QTE from Prestwick or some place to the south." A QTE is radio code for a bearing on an airplane taken from a station. It is created by telepathic sensitivity to the unseen Hertzian electromagnetic waves that gird the earth—cousins of light, outriders of immortality.

"Okay, I'll try Prestwick," says Ernie. "I guess we're close enough now." He throws a switch, tunes in, and takes hold of his key to tap out a message: "5SJ (Prestwick) 5SJ V (from) CHUN (abbreviation for Chocolate Uncle, code name of airplane No. 896) CHUN, K (go ahead.)" Code is usually found more understandable than voice when the radio must reach outward as far as four hundred miles.

In Scotland, still two hours away, Flying Officer Anthony Tweedle sits in the control room at Prestwick. Most of us know him by sight from our intermittent meetings in the dining and lounge rooms at the big Scottish air base. Once I played chess with him while grounded in Prestwick on a foggy afternoon. He is pink-cheeked, slim, and affects a type of fluffy mustache common among those who wear the dusty blue of the Royal Air Force.

It is 02:51 Greenwich Mean Time on this inky black morning of February sixth when Tweedle hears Silvers' message crackle into his head phones. Immediately he keys his perfunctory reply: "CHUN V 5SJ K."

Ernie Silvers then asks: "5SJ V CHUN INT (request) QTE (true bearing on me)."

Responds Tweedle: "CHUN V 5SJ INT QTG (press down your key)."

Ernie holds down his key for thirty seconds: "——V CHUN K."

Whereupon Tweedle records the reading of his sensitive radio compass needle as it points to the source of the distant hum: "262°." He relays this to Silvers as "QTE 262 A (class of dependability of bearing) 0252 (Greenwich Mean Time)."

After tapping out final acknowledgement to Prestwick, Ernie Silvers hands me a slip of paper reading: "QTE, first class—262° on Prestwick at 0252 G.M.T."

"Thanks, Ernie."

It is about now that I notice a few stars winking through the murk. Providential, I decide. Just in time for a fix.

I climb quickly upon my astral stool, set my octant for Alioth in mid-Dipper and start the mechanism. The star sways gently beside the luminous bubble as I collimate it, turning the knob to the right, the left, the right again—holding the bubble's equilibrium like a cyclist coasting down a smooth-paved road. Although at one point Alioth blinks out behind clouds, it reappears in a few seconds—soon enough to save my reading. At two minutes the mechanism stops, I look at my watch, mark the time and altitude, rewind the octant, and start shooting red Antares of Scorpio to the south.

By 3:08 I have plotted the Alioth line of position on my chart, running north and south, and the Antares line running northwest and southeast. So all I need to add is the radio bearing (NE and SW) from Prestwick to make a complete three-line fix, each line corrected for time. The QTE I measure with my protractor at Prestwick, correcting its angle for the distortion of the mercator projection of the chart, and draw the line westward across the Bloody Foreland of Ireland, just as the radio waves carried the signals, until the line meets the two star lines near 54° 30′ North, 13° 00′ West. I remember also to correct the radio bearing line for its passage down the northern Irish coast—because it is true that coast lines tend to bend ratio waves a little, and this tendency must be compensated by good judgment in plotting. My final correction is to move the whole fix about three miles to the right (south) to allow for coriolis, the centrifugal force of the earth's turning.

With the resulting radio-celestial fix I recalculate our groundspeed and make a new estimate of our time of arrival over Nutts Corner range station near Belfast and then Prestwick. This information I pass on to Captain Cloud: "ETA Nutts 04:10, ETA Prestwick 05:06."

Thinking of the radio miracle which has helped make this prophecy, it is a wonder to me that so much practical advantage has already been taken of the earth's mysterious waves and forces and fields about which we know so little. I like to recall the ancient Chinese word for magnet, which is translated as "the stone that loves." For ancients in many countries, and some people today, attribute a soul or a libido to lodestone whose breath "penetrates secretly and with velocity" to draw iron "even as amber attracts mustard seeds."

This naturally magnetic iron ore, magnetite (composed mainly of the oxide Fe_3O_4), indeed appeared to have qualities of spirit which fitted priestly ritual, abetted witch doctors, and gave a patient resolution to the north-pointing needle. There is evidence that the Chinese had won over this strange and steadfast magic with a compass of twenty-four divisions as early as the fifth century, that the Finns and Lapps used a floating needle on their Baltic voyages in A.D. 1000, and the Vikings probably soon after.

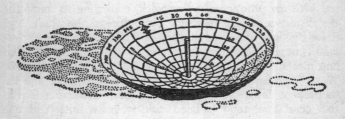

With the understanding of magnetic forces so close to the plinth of navigational science, a navigator is bound almost constantly to engage the unknown, especially in his basic dead reckoning. Like Columbus, every time he looks at his compass he must fend with magnetism. He must make a precise allowance for the fact that the north magnetic pole is some 1350 miles from the north geographic pole. This correction factor, measured in degrees east or west of true north, he knows as "variation."

Isogonic lines, along which the variation is constant, are printed on all navigation charts and they stripe the globe's entire surface in graceful abstruse curves, flowing toward the magnetic poles like spindrift to the Norway maelstrom. The two lines of zero variation, for instance, which are of special attraction to navigators, extend from each magnetic pole to the opposite geographic pole, swooping wildly over the earth's land areas, avoiding the oceans with a strange aversion, passing through all seven continents and veering far afield to touch the areas of densest population. One heads southeast from the north magnetic pole, passing between Detroit and Chicago, down through the industrial United States, across the West Indies and the heart of South America, grazing Buenos Aires on its way. The other goes northwest from the south magnetic pole across Australia to the Dutch East Indies where, curving to the right through the Malay States, Siam, and Indo-China, it swings left around Japan in a great loop like the seam on a baseball, returning southwestward across China, Tibet, Mount Everest, and India between Karachi and Bombay, thence to the horn of Africa and, curving northward, through Egypt and central Europe to the north pole.

No one knows why these mysterious curves of magnetic equilibrium (on which the compass actually points to the true geographic north) cleave so consistently to the habitats of man, including navigators on their days off. Yet they not only exhibit a human bias now but are increasing it with each passing year. For the charts of annual variation change show that the "no variation" line in the United States is moving closer to the crowded northeastern seaboard, in Europe closer to teeming Germany and Italy, and in the Orient closer to Japan and the densely packed Chinese coastal plain.

In places the isogonic lines are moving at a rate of a degree (of variation) every three years, yet in some others no motion at all has been detected. And there are four magnetic neutral spots in the world where the "no motion" lines cross the "no variation" lines, where the local inhabitants can permanently assume their compasses are pointing exactly to the true geographical pole. These favored points, (1) Lake

Michigan, (2) the Bahama Islands, (3) Asmara by the Red Sea, (4) a place in the Pacific Ocean near Japan, are not free of dip, however, which is the tendency of a compass needle to tip from the horizontal as it lines itself up with the magnetic lines.

The basic sources of magnetism in the world are still among the great unknowns that Einstein's successors are trying to fathom along with gravity and other aspects of mass and energy. Magnetism appears fundamental to all matter, for evidence of it has been found everywhere from the nuclei of atoms (where it is measured in "nuclear magnetons") to the most distant galaxies in the sky (where presumably it eventually will be estimated in "galactic magnetons"). And all these systems of matter spin on their private axes and move on their individual orbits—protons expressing their magnetic moments as separately from electrons as stars from their planets, as mesons from neutrinos or photons from gravitons.

Each order of matter seems to be profoundly stirred by the deployment of its ultimate parts into the parallel alignments of magnetism. A metal bar, for instance, undergoes a small but measurable motion when magnetized, as the orbits of its electrons fall into mysterious synchronization, a harmony we can deduce but not yet understand. The earth in its turn literally glows with ionic excitement each time it receives a dose of magnetism from the sun, the glow becoming visible as "northern (or southern) lights" about twenty-five hours after an observed eruption or storm on the sun.

The relationship between the sun spots and magnetic disturbances on earth is already proven beyond question by records of more than one hundred years, so that magnetic observatories now confidently predict electric turmoil in our world when they see the whirling hurricanes of ions lashing outward from the sun at 600 miles a second—invisible tongues of our paternal star speaking to us in atomic language that we cannot evade, showering us with hydrogenic breath until we cannot even understand our own words.

An example of such solar hurly-burly was the famous magnetic storm of Easter Sunday, March 24, 1940, which started all over the earth at 14:00 Greenwich time. At that hour most radio broadcasts suddenly ceased to get across, wired communication became unintelligible, and surprisingly even a number of electric power systems in the United States and Canada went out of order. A message came through on multiplex teletype as follows: GOVE AND EAETER GREETNNGS LROM AGLWGRA CZMGOPBWQQ8TP) ZLQP . . . A telephone conversation between two rapturous persons who thought they were speaking in boudoir privacy somehow got transposed onto a radio program which was heard for one weird minute by several millions. A difference in potential of 800 volts in the earth's electric flow was recorded between New York City and Binghamton, New York, a gradient of 5.7 volts per mile.

When this sort of thing tends to repeat itself in a rhythm of 27 days (the period of the sun's rotation) and again every 11.2 years (the cycle of sunspot maximums) it leaves little doubt as to whence the trouble comes. The less obvious question of just how the fiery electrons crumple the smooth ionization levels of our atmosphere and turn magnetic equilibrium into bubbling pandemonium is hard to answer, but is being investigated from many angles including spectroscopy, astronomy and astrology.

Study of aurora light and analysis of its refracted colors is just another way of looking at the same great mystery of this earthly existence. As we fly regularly from Iceland to Greenland to Labrador or Newfoundland in our weekly rounds, we follow for thousands of miles the belt of most intense auroral visibility, which continues westward across Hudson Bay, Alaska, the Barents Sea and North Cape to Iceland again.

The official average is 243 auroras a year at this magnetic latitude, two nights in every three.

But you don't have to be a researcher to grasp something of the significance of the almost continuous drama we behold here. You can see what it is by its very shape, night after night after night. Almost every time I step into the astrodome on the Iceland-Greenland run I am awed by the auroral majesty above me, by tremendous shapes—green, white, and yellowish pink—arching over the northern horizon and moving stiffly across the heavens on an alarming scale.

The concentric green arcs and rayed bands of course are clearly part of the great oval ring of ionized light created by the entrance of the sun's hydrogen-spray particles into the geomagnetic funnel of our northern sky. Sometimes when we are far enough north to be near the magnetic zenith the parallel rays converging in perspective hundreds of miles up form the rare "corona," which may appear directly overhead as a great yellow wheel with spokes, a pink tiara, or perhaps a sunburst crown of golden light.

More often the aurora just flickers irregularly about the northern half of the sky as though we were lying on a rug of air around the corner from a blazing fire (the hidden sun) watching the firelight dancing upon the ceiling of stars. When I reflect that some of the rays of that strange light have been measured by triangulation to be more than 600 miles up and no part of it ever found lower than 35 miles, the majesty of the aurora becomes almost too much for the mind to encompass.

Astronomers and physicists, however, look upon the phenomenon as just a local example of ionic friction: the collision of solar hydrogen with earthly nitrogen, oxygen, neon and other atmospheric molecules. Their perspective of course has taken on a whole new dimension since artificial satellites started orbiting through space with Geiger counters. And in 1958 physicist James Van Allen discovered that the earth is surrounded by two huge, invisible, doughnut-shaped belts of intense radiation over the equator, one inside the other, the fringes of the outer belt curving down toward the magnetic poles where its spiralling protons crash into our upper atmosphere, intermittently illuminating it by the principle of the neon tube into visible northern and southern lights. But these Van Allen belts are only one dramatic feature of surrounding space which is turning out to contain all sorts of wave-carrying plasmas in a geometry as complex as the maze of nerves and tubes inside the human body.

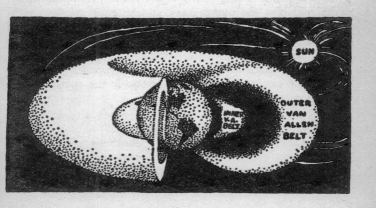

Most people who see the auroral drama hardly have a chance to realize that there is order in its orgy for the patient observer—that, as with a thunderstorm, when you take the time to study out the known causes and effects, you will see an understandable pattern that follows a sequence almost as plain as in a continuous movie. Of course few people watch it long enough to notice this pattern, and they may find themselves coming in at almost any part of the show. Twilight may have raised the curtain past the climax or the first act may not begin until after midnight.

The complete regular program of northern lights commences with a whitish glow. This presently becomes a rising arc which brightens, usually turning yellowish or greenish and breaking into separate parts or cloudlike shapes that wax and wane. The northern boundary (bottom edge unless you are looking from near the north pole) is usually well defined. It lies exactly parallel to the lines of geomagnetic latitude. And when it is very bright the arc normally turns reddish at the bottom and splinters into rays—a smooth curve with searchlight beams diverging from the top. Next the even arch becomes wavy and serpentine, thickening into a rayed blue band and eventually forming the curtains that billow into great flowing folds a thousand miles apart. These tend to move gradually overhead, spreading southward as horseshoe-shaped bands and complicated draperies, with sometimes a corona of rays converging at the zenith, or spider web patterns throbbing slowly to a visual crystalline melody.

At midnight the aurora may appear more to the south than north as successive pulsations of light arise in the southwestern sky to flash eastward, fading into the southeastern horizon. At our distance a rotating sunbeam should sweep by the earth's surface at about 250 miles a second which, sure enough, checks out to be almost precisely the speed of the flashing pulses.

The electromotive force, such as arises when tides of ions play across magnetic lines, like the bowing of violin strings, has its counterpart in the human brain and nerve cords where comparable vibrations create "brainwaves" that can be tuned in on, measured and interpreted by man. The electroencephalograph, for instance, records the brain's tides and weird melodies: the alpha rhythm "resembling a scanning device," the delta wave's "billowy rhythm of sleep," the theta rhythm evoked by repulsion and disappointment, the kappa waves that are most active when cerebral "wheels are grinding" in a conscious effort to remember.

Can it be of less ultimate meaning that epilepsy is being successfully treated as "a temporary electrical storm in the brain," a cross-circuit of billions of neurones? Or insignificant that smell is transmitted by an amplitude modulation (AM) system while most other sensory perceptions reach the brain centers by the static-free frequency modulation (FM) system—firm evidence that the mysterious ocean of thought is alive with hidden waves and different types of current?

If brain waves are so individual that they can be analysed like a kind of subconscious or "automatic" handwriting, who knows but what they will in some cases show responsiveness to faint stimuli like the geomagnetic field. A great deal of evidence has in fact been collected suggesting that some wonderful but still unrecognized organ of both bird and mammalian bodies can do this very thing, enabling homing pigeons and displaced cats to find their way home for hundreds of unfamiliar miles. Come to think of it, there may be no creatures entirely free of this directional sense for it is known among fish, reptiles, insects, humans (especially primitive ones), and probably all vertebrates in varying degrees.

Scottish stags exported to New Zealand have even been found far out at sea, swimming confidently northward—"heading, oblivious of certain death, across the width of the world for their native Scottish hills!"

Most famous of all bumps of locality of course are those possessed by the migrating birds which, far more than the monarch butterfly, the arctic lemming, or the moray eel, find their way almost literally from pole to pole. Some of these have even been observed to go hundreds of miles out of their way in what looks like true "pressure-pattern flying," riding the spring south winds and fall north gales right around the spiraling pressure areas that cross our world, saving whole days of flight time on the bounteous wings of air.

Whose guiding hand directs these sage spirits? What secret navigation needle points the way as they rise wheeling in great questioning circles waiting, waiting for that inner bias of direction? How can the murres of Alaska dive straight through dense sea fog to their lonely island rookeries? What urge brings the penguins of Little America unerring thousands of miles north to Argentina and Brazil—slowly swimming through the sea? Is it like the gathering of lightning that polarizes the cat, this pull of far places and future seasons?

There are probably many kinds of clues that activate the navigational instincts of birds and animals, but the most definitely proven ones are celestial: the sight of the sun by day and the stars by night. Only in 1958 was it conclusively demonstrated that birds inherit an amazing power to recognize star patterns which, combined with an almost equally precise time sense, enables them to find their way wherever they are on earth. Thus even such a tiny creature as the European garden warbler, weighing barely three quarters of an ounce, entirely alone and inexperienced after being released from the cage in which it was born, will fly unerringly from northern Sweden southward across Europe to a particular area in central Africa.

Bird and animal sensitivity to subtle magnetic influences is much less certain but has also been indicated in navigation tests, along with a possible coriolis instinct that would amount to an awareness of the direction of the turning of the earth—and perhaps even a power of tuning in on unknown kinds of radiation or still more mysterious so-called telepathic sources. Any combination of these mediums of navigation now seems within the range of conceivability and they fit in curiously with the communication system known to be used by some species of moths, a system that suggests again and again a meaningful similarity between the devices of ancient nature and modern man: a kind of bug radio that actually broadcasts messages of love on infra-red wave lengths, the exact frequency being determined not by dial knob but by the length of antenna used, each female moth anxiously tuning in on a male moth with just the right amount of palp to receive what he can send with his pre-tuned flying radio set.

An excellent example of the influence of mysterious and spiritual things on navigation occurred about fifteen years ago to a navigator friend of mine named Willie Leveen. Willie was inadvertently cast in the leading role in a living nightmare over the British Isles one stormy night near the end of World War II. His was a true-life adventure which may well take its proper place in history as a modern navigation classic.

Willie had been my radio instructor in the last months of 1943 and he had served American Airlines as a crack radio operator during most of the war. He had learned navigation only in the early months of 1944. The occasion of his great adventure was his fifth transoceanic trip as a navigator, under the Air Transport Command, when he was flying a cargo of "eighteen American generals" from the Azores to Prestwick. The Battle of the Bulge was less than a month away and this heavy helping of high brass was just returning from a final conference with General Marshall at the Pentagon.

Willie's weather folder showed a severe cold front approaching Britain from the west but it was not due to hit Scotland for at least an hour after the plane's arrival there, so he was not particularly concerned. The long afternoon dragged on uneventfully until the sun, seen withershins from the airplane, swiftly settled into the western ocean. Then suddenly night closed down like an eyelid upon the seeing earth, Ireland was still three hours away and, as the first stars appeared, Willie could see a dense cloud bank far ahead—the rear of the cold front.

Knowing that he had little time left in which to get a celestial position, he quickly picked out several well-dispersed stars and shot himself a good four-star fix. The position showed the airplane practically on course and substantiated his 1:05 A.M. ETA on Prestwick.

By the time Willie had worked out the fix it was nearly ten o'clock and the airplane had entered the cloud bank. There was now nothing left to navigate with but the radio and dead reckoning. The flight was still going according to plan, however, and neither Willie nor his pilot, Captain Daniel L. Boone, had any apprehension of serious trouble. One of the generals sitting in the passengers' cabin was amusing himself by keeping track of the headings of the airplane, aided by his own pocket compass and watch. The airplane was a Douglas C–54 and her code name was Great Joy Queen.

After about an hour Willie got a radio bearing from the range station at Valley, in northern Wales. It gave him a line of position that plotted at right angles to his course, an indication of groundspeed. But Willie didn't rate it of much value because radio could not be relied on at two hundred miles out, and besides, the line, if correct, showed that Great Joy Queen must have slowed down to an almost absurd degree.

As the next hour passed, Willie kept expecting better radio reception, but neither he nor his radioman could raise a thing. They couldn't even get Valley any more. "Mighty strange," thought Willie. "Could the radio be on the blink?" Not likely, as all three radios on board acted the same. An eerie loneliness came over Willie as he looked out into the black nothingness beyond the windows, and heard the sound of sizzling fat in his ear phones.

He leaned over Captain Boone's shoulder: "We still can't get a thing on the radio, Dan. All I've got is dead reckoning. Do you think we could climb out of this soup and get a star shot?"

"Not a chance, Willie," said Boone. "This cumulus stuff goes way up. Better stick to D.R. and keep trying the radio."

So Willie kept to his original flight plan, using dead reckoning, guessing the wind from the weather folder carried all the way from the Azores. He also kept at the radio. He worked the command set while the radio man worked the liaison set. Between them they tried the automatic radio compasses too, even the loop. They tried everything. But, as Willie said afterward, "no dice."

Landfall had been estimated for about 12:00 P.M., so after midnight Willie assumed Ireland was below. What else could he do? And when the time came, according to flight plan and dead reckoning, he made the turn over the range station at Nutts Corner, heading northeast for Prestwick. Of course he had no check as to whether he really was anywhere near Nutts Corner, but when you don't *know* something in such a case you have to *assume* something. It's at least a hypothesis until proven or disproven—for you can't stop and ponder when you're moving at 180 knots.

As the Queen flew northeastward toward a hypothetical Prestwick, and still no radio, Willie wondered what to do next. He had long since passed his point of no return, so there was no chance of going back to the Azores. His alternate destination of Valley was still a possibility but without radio would be no easier to find than Prestwick.

Should he try to descend under the clouds and find Prestwick visually? No. With only a vague idea of where he was and no knowledge of whether there was any room between clouds and earth, descending blindly down into mountainous Scotland would be almost as sensible as diving out an office window in New York City in hopes of landing in a haystack.

Then what about going up? It offered small hope and would use a lot of gasoline, but men in dire straits must grasp for anything. Willie again put it to Boone.

"No," said the captain. "There must be something you can get on the radio. Radio's our best bet for getting down, Willie. Even a three-star fix can't show us the way down through this soup—but radio can."

So Willie and his radioman twirled the knobs some more. Was there any station at all on the air? Evidently not one . . . No. Nothing. No—yes, there was one. But it was hard to tell whether it was a voice or dots and dashes. Then it was gone. The static sounded like a crackling fire. For millions of miles outward toward the sun the unseen sky was filled with hydrogen ions whipping downward upon the earth, playing hob with magnetic stability around both temperate zones. Scotland was almost in the band of maximum disturbance.

Willie switched on the radio compass again, tuned to Prestwick. The dead needle started breathing, twitched, and moved. Then it reversed itself, wavered and spun around three times . . .

Willie wished he had radar aboard. Radar might just have worked in a time like this. What a help it would have been to get a radar reflection back from the ground, to feel out those craggy Scottish hills a little. But the lesson of Job, "Speak to the earth, and it shall teach thee," had not yet been learned by this flying boxcar.

Nor was there yet any loran on this four-engined sky horse —loran, the new visual radio that since World War II has widely simplified long-range navigation, permitting quick fixes of position by electronic measurements of micro-second intervals between pairs of synchronized stations.

Willie wasted no thought yearning for this fluoroscopic magic that was already enabling other navigators to home in on special loran charts of hyperbolas in many colors—this ballet of the pine needles, of shimmering sky waves, subsea grass and green fire, of storms and snakes and music and lightning standing still. He knew that he couldn't have gotten a fix on the best loran set in the world under the magnetic pandemonium now enveloping his world. Loran was too new, too delicate, too tricky still—and anyhow he didn't have it.

So, "What about it, Dan?" asked Willie once more. "Want to go up? Not a prayer on the radio."

"Let's try the Irish Sea," said Captain Boone. "That's right here somewhere to the west of us. It would be pretty safe to let down there to a couple of thousand feet and maybe we can get on contact and see our way into Prestwick."

"All right," said Willie. "Better fly two-seventy. I don't like this much."

Boone adjusted the throttle knobs and started letting down, turning to a course of 270°. Willie watched anxiously.

Down and down— . . . 8000 feet . . . 5000 feet . . .

3000 feet . . . 2000 . . . 1500 . . . Finally Boone leveled off, but still there was no bottom to the clouds.

"You win, Willie," he said. "I guess we have no choice now."

He set his throttles for a long climb. Presently all the men adjusted their oxygen masks and opened the valves for higher altitude. Willie and the radio man kept their ear phones on, kept trying everything in the book—but heard only the wail of the unknown void around them, the unearthly howl of outraged electrons flying from the sun. And the altimeter needle moved slowly upwards: 15,000 feet . . . 16,000 . . . 17,000 . . .

After a long half hour Great Joy Queen was getting close to her ceiling, and still in the clouds which seemed to have no end. The needle read 25,200 feet and the big plane was beginning to mush. There was hardly enough air to hold her up, but somehow she managed to claw her way among the molecules of nitrogen still a little higher—25,400—and a little higher—25,500 . . . 25,550 . . .

Willie was beside himself with anxiety, and consciously appealed to what divine powers there might be in the great unknown vastness above and all around. Could he have a peek at a star? Just a few seconds of a star? Just one little star. Any star would do. Anything would do, please God.

As Dan Boone labored toward the last inch of ceiling, Willie's gray eyes scanned the dark nothingness out of the astrodome—wistfully, pleadingly, desperately. Was there a light anywhere? A whisper of a star? Now was the crucial time. Now, God.

What was that over there to the east? The frost on the dome? Willie rubbed the frozen breath with his sleeve. And there was still something light up there: the moon!

Ah! Willie thanked God in his heart as he reached for his octant and swung it toward the hazy glow of light. It was the full moon. It was dim and vague but strangely big—as big as a parson's barn—almost too big. The sky was still deep in clouds but now and then Willie could see its roundness clear enough to shoot. He quickly removed his oxygen mask to clear his face for the piece.

"Hold her steady, Dan," he called as he balanced the silver bubble and pressed his trigger on the moon. It was the most difficult shot Willie had ever made—and the most fraught with consequence. The angle twisted his neck and he was cold. Besides, he could hardly make out the moon's limb and he had to keep rubbing the frost off the Plexiglas every fifteen seconds, the while dancing on his little stool. He didn't have the traditional electric hair dryer for cooking the frost off the dome. He just rubbed with one hand, desperately. Without oxygen, his breath came in short gasps.

Somehow he managed it, and as Boone started descending again Willie figured and plotted a moon line. But as his fingers drew the line Willie's eyes widened with amazement. The line was mostly off the map. It ran north and south and put the plane somewhere just off the coast of Norway!

"Dan, do a one-eighty turn and let down," gasped Willie. He half expected Boone to question his wild request, but Boone promptly banked the plane into a complete reversal of direction and the Queen was headed southwest, presumably back across the North Sea toward Britain again. "We must be in one hell of a west wind," muttered Willie.

When he was asked later by investigators why he accepted that single implausible moon shot as accurate, Willie replied, "It was all I had had to go by in more than four hours. What else could I believe?"

Fortunate it was for the war and at least two dozen lives that Willie had that much confidence in himself, and that Boone trusted him too—for fate was figuring close that night, and there were only a couple of hours of gasoline left.

As the plane descended steadily toward what Willie presumed was the North Sea, Boone throttled down his engines to save every possible drop of fuel. He put her on maximum range. That is the slow overdrive prop and throttle setting of lean mixture (more air and less gas) originated by Pan American, with Lindbergh as advisor, for just such an emergency. It means flying just slow enough to squeeze as many miles out of each gallon as you can without mushing.

The plan was to try to get below the clouds and the strong winds while over the sea where it would be reasonably safe to descend that low. To do this Willie had to bet the lives of all on board on his moon shot. The war in France might also feel the consequences. He had to wager everything on coming down to the sea rather than into rugged Norway, Scotland, or the Orkney Isles.

Down, down they went. When the altimeter showed 500 feet, anxiety became intense. If over land, this altitude could easily be disastrous—and Willie could not even judge the accuracy of the altimeters because he had received no barometric correction since the Azores.

At "400 feet" a grayness appeared in the black below. The sea! Willie relaxed a little. Boone leveled off at 200 feet where he could avoid the full force of the evident headwinds of higher levels. Willie gazed anxiously at the water. He thought he could see huge white caps: a gale blowing from the west.

Consulting with Boone, Willie had determined to fly west until the British coast appeared, then fly along the coast in an attempt to recognize some locality and, if possible, find a landing field. Meanwhile the flight clerk and engineer were making preparation for possible landing in the sea. Life rafts were dragged forth and Mae West jackets handed to all the generals. It is interesting to think of the comments that must have come from the brass as they were being assigned individually to rafts. Of that, alas, I have no record.

After a half hour Boone suddenly cried, "Land!" He banked to the right and headed up the coast. All the crew looked eagerly at the dim outline of the shore and Willie tried to match it with some part of his map. It was tantalizing. He could not recognize anything, nor tell whether the coast was England, Scotland, the Shetlands, or even something else. Willie felt cold shivers in his bones.

Soon realizing the unlikelihood of identifying the blacked-out coast in time to do any good, Willie decided it would be better to go inland in search of airfields and possible radio contact. So he got Boone to turn west, and they agreed to fly inland for thirty minutes. If they could not discover anything useful in that time they would return to the coast. By then, they figured, the fuel tanks would be about empty. They planned in the end to ditch in the ocean as close to land as possible in hopes of being able to make the shore in their rubber rafts against the gale blowing out to sea.

As they flew west Willie and the radio man continued trying everything in the book on their radios, desperately seeking even the faintest recognizable response. And Willie peered ahead at the same time over Boone's shoulder watching the murky landscape below for a light or a city, a railroad line, a highway, a lake—any clue.

At one point Willie suddenly saw a high hill approaching dead ahead. It was so close he was sure they would crash. He braced himself frantically as Boone zoomed upward and the "hill" burst all around them! It was a black cloud—and in four seconds they were out again on the other side. Hard on the nerves, this.

Every now and then Willie would look at the radio compass—just in case it should settle down and come to the point. It was still spinning now and wavering except when passing through clouds, he noticed. Sometimes large cumulus clouds have enough current in them to activate the radio compass and thunderstorms have been known to masquerade as range stations. So he watched and checked and waited for identification—and listened—and looked some more.

What was that whine in the headphones? Was it Scotland or Norway or Russia? Willie could not decide whether the radio sounded more like bagpipes or Tchaikowsky's Chinese dance. It would have been funny if only it had not been so serious.

When the allotted thirty minutes were nearly gone, the radioman suddenly shouted, "Prestwick! I've got Prestwick!" It was now 4:30 A.M. and this was the first radio contact made in five and a half hours. The sputtering code sang forth as in the Psalm: "He spake to them in the cloudy pillar." Willie prayed it would not prove too late.

The radioman tapped out a request for position. A couple of minutes passed while Prestwick control and other co-ordinated stations took simultaneous bearings on the airplane; then the position was given in exact latitude and longitude.

Willie scribbled it down: "3° 35' W., 53° 20' N."

"Dan," he shouted, "do a one-eighty. We're headed for Ireland. We're over the Irish Sea near Liverpool."

Willie had to think hard. He knew where he was at last, but there was so little gas left that it seemed out of the question to try to reach Prestwick. Some nearer field would have to be found. But the radio was still scarcely usable and very uncertain.

As the Queen approached land again Willie racked his brain for ideas. He remembered vaguely having heard of an emergency radio system the R.A.F. used for helping disabled bombers find their way home. It was known by the code name of "Darkee." It was the emergency Darkee System, but how could Willie find it? What was the frequency?

Willie found himself praying again. "Dear God, we need You still." There was not a minute to lose. And to Willie's amazement an answer popped into his head at once: 4220 kilocycles. "It came straight from the Lord," he told me afterward.

Willie's fingers twirled the knobs to 4220 and held down the microphone button: "Darkee, Darkee, Darkee—"

He got an answer: "This is Darkee! Circle. Circle. We are tracking you . . . Now we have you. Fly one-twenty degrees. We will give you further instructions. Altimeter setting is 29.31. Highest obstruction four hundred feet."

Willie leaned over Boone's shoulder as Boone flew the course of 120°. He corrected the altimeters to 29.31 for existing barometric pressure, and Boone kept the Queen at 600 feet. It was so dark that scarcely anything of the landscape below could be seen and often it was obscured by fog or low clouds. Time went by . . . fifteen minutes . . . twenty minutes . . .

Just when Willie was beginning to expect splutters from the engines as the fuel tanks went dry, Darkee said: "Make a three-sixty turn. You are over the field. Let down to five hundred feet."

Boone did as he was told, but could see nothing of the ground. "Darkee, we are still in solid clouds," he reported.

"Then go down to four hundred," said Darkee.

When even that failed to reveal the ground, Darkee urged, "Three hundred feet, but very carefully."

Again Boone crept downward, feeling his way with eyes now on the altimeter, now on the blackness beyond the windshield. When the needle read 300, the clouds remained as impenetrable as ever.

"Still can't see you, Darkee."

"I can hear you plainly," said Darkee. "You are south of the tower now, about two miles. Fly thirty degrees. That will bring you over the tower."

Boone banked quickly until his compass showed 30°. In less than a minute Darkee said, "Now you are exactly above me. Circle to the right and let down to two hundred feet."

Boone nosed downward again and at 200 feet saw what seemed to be an opening in the murk. Venturing to 150 feet he could dimly make out the ground at times, but no sign of an airport.

"Where is the runway, Darkee? Will you shoot off a flare for us?"

A beautiful green flame rocketed into the sky from almost directly below.

"We are right over you, Darkee, but can't see any runway."

"The runway is below you now. Circle and land! You will see it. Circle and land!"

As Boone circled desperately once more, Willie noticed that the fuel gauges read zero. Still no runway in sight. Long afterward Boone was to write me: "When I think about it I get a sick feeling in the pit of my stomach."

"We are going to land anyway," cried Boone. "Give us all the lights you've got, Darkee. We are out of gas. We have no choice."

Just then there was a sputter from number four engine and it quickly died. Boone circled to the left—descending—apprehensively searching. Suddenly two lines of lights appeared below. The runway! By some strange quirk of mind Darkee had forgotten in his excitement to turn on the lights until now. Skillfully swinging around to line up with the runway, Daniel Boone put her gear down and brought the Queen in on three engines, easing her steeply into the little field, an R.A.F. fighter base. The wheels touched, bounced. She was rolling fast and the runway was short. The brakes squealed and smoked and Boone pulled his emergency bottle, a hydraulic device that locks the brakes—something to be used only under desperate circumstances.

When the big plane finally screeched to rest at the very end of the runway, Boone swung her around to taxi to the ramp. It was only then that Willie noticed that number three engine was also dead. And by the ramp the other two engines had started to sputter. The tanks were dry. They had landed in the little town of Downham Market, eighty miles north of London.

When I last saw Willie a few months ago, he was just out of the hospital after a nearly fatal accident in which his car was hit by a big grocery truck. He had broken a leg and an arm, several ribs, fractured his skull badly and, as in the adventure over Britain, had escaped only with the skin of his soul.

As we walked across Union Square in New York City to lunch I noticed Willie would not venture a foot from the curb until the lights were indubitably in our favor. "I'm not taking any chances," said Willie reverently. "God has always pulled me through the pinches, and I'm not gonna put undue strain on our relations."

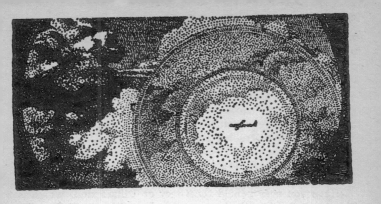

14

Beyond the Rainbow

SOMETIMES I FEEL a strange exhilaration up here which seems to come from something beyond the mere stimulus of flying. It is a feeling of belonging to the sky I fly, of owning and being owned—if only for a moment—by the air I breathe. It is akin to the well-known claim of the swallow: each bird staking out his personal bug-strewn slice of heaven, his inviolate property of the blue.

Even though we cannot stop up here, not even stop to think, but must snatch what ideas and dreams we may on the wing, we do take fleeting possession of much airy territory. It is ephemeral to be sure, like all possession, we to it and it to us, yet the substance of it is vast in scope, unlimited in potentiality, teeming with stimulation, and its every kilo-acre is incontestably ours to use while we can—to drink in, to snuff up, to sort and savor and exhale, to void to the void again.

This transitory quality of the atmosphere is parcel of change in a rapid volatile realm. By the time the next fellow roars along, the sky is not the sky we knew. Literally the elements of it, the nitrogen and oxygen, the ozone and krypton, have moved off and rearranged themselves. Even the light rays from the sun are redistributed, refracted, rediffused.

More than most things of the sky, rainbows seem to be peculiarly our own. And, as if to prove it, they follow us through the sky instead of dropping behind like clouds and vapor trails—almost as if they were of the mind rather than the body. This is true of many optical effects of course, but of nothing more than the rare and lovely rainbows and mist-bows, the coronas and halos we see so often in the humid sky.

Have you ever beheld the Glory or Ulloa's rind, which is known in the Alps as "the spectre of the Brocken"? It is the ultimate rainbow, a complete set of circles of spectral colors known only to those who fly or to mountaineers. We see it moving against cloud layers below us when rain is on our shady side. It seems to bend and wave through fleeing empty air. It is as different from the common terrestrial rain-bow that forms an arch as the full moon is different from the one-day crescent. Like an elusive color target it speeds in concentric circles along the flanks of clouds on the opposite side from the sun, matching our pace, weaving and dancing in perfect time with our shadow—the small shadow of the airplane remaining constantly in the exact illuminated center of the Glory.

I think the central aura of this spectacle was named the Glory by Samuel Taylor Coleridge who described the spectre of the Brocken as "an image with a glory round its head," for its resemblance to ecclesiastical pictures of holy persons has been remarked by many and interpreted by not a few as a vision of divine portent.

The flowing whitish corona about the seer's shadow in the center has the interesting quality of appearing closer than its surrounding rainbows or mistbows, and may well be really nearer on the average—even though rainbows on the ground have been measured as close as six feet from the viewer. The rainbow dimensions of greatest certainty seem to be the angles between the primary and secondary bows and the anti-solar point, which is the center of the observer's own shadow directly opposite the sun.

It is just 42° from the anti-solar point to the main (primary) rainbow, which can be defined as that cone surface (apparently a circle) in which all the rain drops are at the best angle both to reflect and refract sunlight toward your eye at the cone's apex. The rainbow in other words has as great a depth as the extent of the rain and it therefore exists more in a direction than in a location. This is so literally true that each eye actually sees its own separate three-dimensional rainbow, and I have clearly seen two such conic bows (right and left) in the spray of a hose in a sunny garden.

The spectral hues of all rainbows of course result from natural white sunlight's being composed of various wave lengths of unequal refrangibility which refract at slightly different angles, becoming bands of red, orange, yellow, green, blue, and violet light like Easter eggs sorted by an egg grader. As if it were not wonderful enough to have this happen at the anti-solar angle of 42° where the light reflects *once* off the back of each falling drop of rain, passing through the lenslike water in coming and going, it happens also where the light bounces *twice* off the back surface—in this case hitting your eye at the anti-solar angle of 51°.

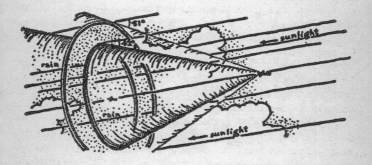

That is the explanation for the secondary rainbow, fainter than the first and 9° further from your anti-solar shadow—which puts it outside the main bow in our sky, or above it as seen from the ground where the anti-solar point is below the horizon. Half a degree is about as close as one can figure these effects because the sun source of light is not a single point but has a diameter of 31' of arc.

Rainbows naturally vary in color balance and character as well as direction, for the condition of the atmosphere modulates the light waves that make them. The size of rain drops affects them so directly that a meteorologist with training in spectroscopy can tell by the distribution of colors exactly how big the rain is and how fast it is falling. Big drops (.04—.10 inches diameter) make predominantly red rainbows with bright violet and green lines but faint blue; smaller drops produce less red; very small drops (.002 inches) make a rainbow with a distinct white stripe. Mistbows, reflected off still smaller drops, pale down through solid white toward transparency in the dim fogbow which retains only the faintest orange and bluish edges, while the microscopic droplets of pure cloud flesh (.0001 inches) will not support any rainbow at all.

The experts also study the polarization of rainbow light, which is considerable, and an eminent mathematician appropriately named Airy (Sir George Biddell Airy, British astronomer royal) derived from rainbow refraction theory a century ago the famous rainbow integral

$$A = c \int_0^\infty \cos \frac{\pi}{2} (u^3 - zu) du$$

which, for my money, is obviously better suited to remaining a divine recipe for rainbows than to being analyzed as a secular equation in optical calculus.

The modern era in physics began about 1895 when the idea of substance in the material world gave way to the idea of behavior. A new perspective appeared in the world. Matter, which had seemed to be composed of particles, began to give "contrary" evidence of being made up of mysterious wave motions. Was matter really made of solid bits of something? Or just intangible waves of energy? Or was the atom built on what Eddington later was to call "wavicles," mysterious particles that vibrated like waves?

Physicists today are still wrestling with these basic questions. If matter is made of particles, what are particles made of? If an electron is nothing but a charge of electricity, what is electricity: stuff, or energy, or imagination? Is it tangible or intangible, acute or obtuse, concrete or abstract? Is it more than a dream of consciousness that creates its own existence? Is it some mysterious essence of the time-space continuum? Or is our limited notion of time or space too meagre an abstraction? Does the revolution of an electron in its orbit around a proton actually consume an atomic year?

The old-fashioned Euclidean "space of common sense" has irretrievably exploded into Riemannian geometry (of multi-dimensional space) and all sorts of new mathematical concepts from Veblen's geometry of spinors to Boolean and lattice algebras and the calculus of variations. These imaginative methods of thinking tend to increase at the same time that light, gravity, time, energy and electromagnetic phenomena are being synthesized into a single generalized theory, even though Einstein and Eddington do not think brain to brain as to what kind of new geometry is best for the job. Mathematics in their minds seems to be reaching below logic toward the more basic authority of feeling, becoming less of a science and more of an art. Einstein "dislikes" certain trains of thought even though they are logical, while Eddington frankly admits the most advanced and profound mathematical choices are basically "a matter of taste." Sir James Jeans, expressing it still another way, declares the ultimate nature of the universe to be "mental"—which is at least a goodly step toward uniting science with religion.

What are the limits of strength or beauty in this earth world, in this human shade of living? Clearly we cannot know—yet. But the hints we find in faith and music, in love and glimpses of glory promise much more beyond the mortal veil than we could possible absorb here. Here the dainty capacity of our infantile souls requires that they be sheltered not only against the alluring opportunities outside the eggshell of death but also from the full present sufferings of other souls still on earth.

In the larger view our first five senses are but crude tools indeed. I suppose they could be considered spiritual rattles or psychic teddy bears of this astral nursery, yet they have the important function of teaching us a wide variety of elementary lessons.

In an effort to project ourselves toward our ultimate imagination, our eventual soul sight, we may reasonably attempt to sense the first simple dimensions of God. We must realize of course that, by the very definition of His name, we cannot possibly fathom Him entire. Probably not His billionth part nor, mathematically speaking, even $1/N^{nth}$ of His N^{nth} degree. But yet logic and faith and humility and imagination and reverence may give us a sometime gleanth.

God could not be restricted to a preconceived limitation of experience, to having to be only one consciousness or personality at a time, or even to having to enter our supposed time-space relativity at all.

From the deepest perspective could it not be possible then that we ourselves—you and I—are an actual part of God's experience, a small yet significant part—that He feels and knows eternally through our senses, our lives, our aspirations, our sacrifices, our creations, along with all such everywhere, everywhen? Which of His prophets has not said as much? For God could not logically be the true Creator unless creatures existed. Even our own small creations in turn then could be looked upon as inevitable sub-reflections of His creatorship. Collectively we are surely some sort of aspect of total divinity, just as the universe is not only God's physical body (His material manifestation) but a vital frame of reference like the white of this page that imparts to these black letters their readability.

Trying to fathom such profundities here in the moving heavens necessarily involves a new perspective on time. For if God's experience, essentially complete and therefore past in respect to Him, is also our experience, it is just as surely incomplete and therefore present in respect to us.

I used to think of the passage of time as a steady motion, harnessed to the constant speed of rotation of the earth and its revolutions around the sun. But up here I am coming to see it as not constant but accelerating. Assuredly clock time as known to children and geographers is an elementary, finite truth, but that can hardly be all that the human mind and spirit are capable of, even in this present life. Time already seems to me more realistically an explosion of the finite into the infinite, an acceleration in which visible outer space symbolizes the past accelerating outward into the present, and deducible subatomic inner space the present accelerating toward the future. As outer space expands at its accelerating velocity it reaches unknowability when its outward rate overtakes the speed of light and its light can no longer come to our material eyes. Beyond that lies only imagination and the great mystery of things outside our definable material universe. So also with time and its dimensions above our mortal span, beyond the few billion years of physical measurability on our astronomical clock.

Yet since time has no proven existence apart from the sequence of events (events in the mechanisms of clocks, in the evolutions of stars . . .) all God has to do to change or end time is to change or end the sequence of events. And that is just what He seems to be doing—as it looks from here. By a great but little appreciated natural law He is steadily accelerating time (relative to consciousness) toward simultaneity, toward the infinite.

Hardly any fully grown person can have failed to notice that each year (on the average) goes by a little faster than the one before. This obviously must be because each additional year is a smaller portion of our total experience. It is also by way of being a natural device of growth and education, for how else could the newborn baby find time enough to take everything in? What clearer introduction to his first year than a leisurely taste of a long second, a slow drinking in of a full minute, then a whole event-filled hour, building up to a day, a week, a month—gradually demonstrating the larger and larger meaning of time? Space too, the same way: an easy inch, a big foot, a long yard . . . an interminable mile . . .

Things naturally seem static to a year-old baby. To him Mother is just Mother. She is always the same: never was different, never will be different. Or so it seems. He has not lived long enough to notice much change in anything or anybody. A year to him naturally feels a lifetime. A year literally is his lifetime—to date.

When a man arrives at the age of eighty, on the other hand, the clock has grown to be moving very fast by comparison. Nothing is static any more. His old friends are dying almost every day. New children sprout into adults like spring flowers. Strange buildings pop up like mushrooms. A whole year to him now actually consumes less conscious time than did five days when he was one year old. A year has become scarcely more than one per cent of his total memory.

If you can project your mind beyond death, imagine now how time must fly for a man who has lived a million years. If the same acceleration has continued, a year by then will have been reduced to a mere one millionth part of his total experience, the equivalent of thirty-one seconds to the one-year-old. Babies will grow to manhood in ten minutes and die of old age before breakfast.

Ultimately, as the natural law prevails, whole generations will pass like flashes of lightning. Eons will drift by like time-lapse movies of civilization on the march, evolution evolving before your eyes. Birth and death will merge into a simultaneous whole and time itself will reveal at last its full stature as a dimension of development while total experience will blossom easily from the finite into the increasingly-imaginable perspectives of infinity.

Although the real purpose of clock time, our current finite time (which will ultimately be relegated to a spicy epoch of deep antiquity), thus seems to be to give us beginners a chance to sort out our experiences while learning them, we do not have to lose the minute as we gain the hour. Nor let go the year to grasp the century. I can actually read a chapter of the book of life now in the same number of clock hours it took me to read a single sentence in my childhood, yet I think I understand most sentences of that chapter much better than I understood the single sentence I struggled with of yore. So the accleration of the years need not take away comprehension or appreciation. Quite the reverse. I am rash enough to predict that when you and I are a billion earth years old and a finite century unrolls in a twinkle, we will still have ample "time" to take in every minute of every year.

What profits us then to wager for glory on earth, for renown between year X and year Y on the time clock? To the understanding of infinity any hour is zero. For infinity divided by a number (of hours, years, centuries) remains imperturbably infinity.

Undoubtedly the day will come, and rather sooner than we think, when our spiritual maturity will be glad our bodies have been left behind—those childish toys that were becoming anchors to hold back our deepening experience. Most of us will need to be old in years, perhaps outside death's shell, to have gained that much perspective of our mortal limitations—yet sooner or later it will come to us all. It may be our first great realization beyond the grave. We will then awake from the dream of finite time-space into a totally different order of comprehension. Perhaps our minds will drift outward from our outmoded cerebrums like magnetic fields escaping an unplugged electronic computer, permitting us to recognize at a thought other souls we have known before.

More generally accepted by science, however, is the growing realization that, since matter remains unprovable, elusive, and largely theoretical, life itself consists mainly in the tuning in for a time of the appropriate harmonics among the atoms. This is to say that out of the myriads of vibrations and waves everywhere, some few in some mysterious manner tune in on certain combinations of organic carbon molecules, giving them the magic lease we sense as life. Such an ephemeral pattern of orbits thus becomes the protoplasm of an ear-wig, a lily, a bird, a man. It grows into physical being, a meeting place of ideas, a U.N. of consciousness. Yet what is its essence? What makes it alive? Being a group of cells temporarily assembled, it is in a curious way suggestive of a radio. Radio-like, it responds to mysterious and remote stimuli, perhaps expressing itself extravagantly for a few years, ending in a sudden breakdown of parts which cuts it off from its source of power so that it turns cold and silent unto "death."

Does a snowflake with its faint electromagnetic aura thus tune in on the carbon of human flesh: twirling its lacy dial to call Carbon 6—66 ring 3? Can the impulses in nerves be compared to the discharges of lightning in the sky? Muscles to towering clouds, blood to warm rain, breath to the wind?

It seems silly that men down there greet birth with smiles, with cigar passings and congratulations, while death brings forth only frustration, crepe and remorse. All because growth is considered good while decay is bad and unhealthy, something to fight against to the inevitable, the bitter, bitter end.

Do they forget that decay begins at conception if not before? That decay is the smell of the rose, the flame of the maple in October, and the inseparable partner of growth, both being vital to life?

Perhaps their blindness to a healthy and beautiful death is necessary to their own growth, the sowing of the larger soul. Who knows the true worth of waste and war and greed, of misplaced trust and fanatic love? Let folly live that spirit may be born. Is the population of cells that is I more than a whirlpool of vibration, an intersection of waves, a magnetic storm, the breath of a star? Is oxygen part of this body it passes through? Does the sky itself sing the song of life?

Death is not the reverse of life, but its unfolding—a sometime equalizer of growth and decay.

Wallowing along at a languid hundred and seventy knots at our thought-engendering altitude, I feel ofttimes as if I were back in the crosstrees of my youth, my weather eye upon the soft horizon, musing on the mirror-illusion of this mortal world where day is balanced against night, male against female, land against sea, flow against ebb. It was the budding of new paradox then. It appears the flowering of mature mystery now.

I learn that the material in space, including stars and planets, is spread more thinly on the average than the highest vacuum that can be created on earth. Yet this unearthly emptiness contains all the matter there is—all the stuff of all the worlds. What substance then or import in the vacuous ocean of truth has the mortal earth? Or you? Or I?

All the little lessons are here before our eyes. If you would shield yourself with mortal armor, observe the limitations of the turtle and the lobster. If you prefer a liquid body to avoid being pinched in the door or stuck with a dagger, consider the jellyfish. If you would regenerate yourself to get back an amputated leg or arm, consult the angle worm. If you would learn patience, control, design, study the spider. Even navigation is taught here by methods more advanced than man's—by the migrating birds of the sky, by the homing fish in the deep. And what better than the stars as object lessons in perspective—than birth for exercise in humility—than death for a seminar in giving?

As if to remind me that the sky over Belfast was still part of the mortal world, our left wing dipped just noticeably as we turned the corner to let down over the North Channel, heading for the Firth of Clyde. It was 04:08 G.M.T. Soon we would land by Orangefield Castle at the Prestwick Air Base. Blake Cloud drank the last of his cold coffee, set the cup back on the pedestal where the spoon purred in quiet sympathy with our four throttled engines.

As I checked my instruments again, recorded 460 gallons of fuel remaining, and tried to catch up on my log, I noticed we were descending through a flat sheet of silky alto-stratus cloud like a prairie of snow yet so thin I could see below it the flamfoo of moonshine upon the restless waters around Ailsa Craig. The sight of the tall lonely Scottish rock was reassuring, even with the full wind upon it—perhaps, more truly, *because* of the wind.

It was a pale incorporeal wind that seemed to penetrate the earth and every breathing thing upon the face of the earth—blowing as it has blown through all memory and song. I could feel it bearing the body of the airplane within its own body, gently yawing, softly rocking the babe of man safe inside his mother sky—while everywhere the embracing lullaby of wind swept on, coming from we know not where, going we know not whence—inexorable, aloof, of a mind apart.

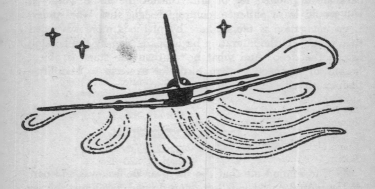

Index

THE AVIATOR'S BOOKSHELF
THE CLASSICS OF FLYING

The books that aviators, test pilots, and astronauts feel tell the most about the skills that launched mankind on the adventure of flight. These books bridge man's amazing progress, from the Wright brothers to the first moonwalk.

☐ **THE WRIGHT BROTHERS by Fred C. Kelly** (23962-7 • $2.95)
Their inventive genius was enhanced by their ability to learn how to fly their machines.

☐ **THE FLYING NORTH by Jean Potter** (23946-5 • $2.95)
The Alaskan bush pilots flew in impossible weather, frequently landing on sandbars or improvised landing strips, flying the early planes in largely uninhabited and unexplored land.

☐ **THE SKY BEYOND by Sir Gordon Taylor** (23949-X • $2.95)
Transcontinental flight required new machines piloted by skilled navigators who could pinpoint tiny islands in the vast Pacific—before there were radio beacons and directional flying aids.

☐ **THE WORLD ALOFT by Guy Murchie** (23947-3 • $2.95)
The book recognized as *The Sea Round Us* for the vaster domain—the Air. Mr. Murchie, a flyer, draws from history, mythology and many sciences. The sky is an ocean, filled with currents and wildlife of its own. A tribute to, and a celebration of, the flyers' environment.

☐ **CARRYING THE FIRE by Michael Collins** (23948-1 • $3.50)
"The best written book yet by any of the astronauts."—*Time Magazine*. Collins, the Gemini 10 and Apollo 11 astronaut, gives us a picture of the joys of flight and the close-in details of the first manned moon landing.

☐ **THE LONELY SKY by William Bridgeman with Jacqueline Hazard** (23950-3 • $3.50)
The test pilot who flew the fastest and the highest. The excitement of going where no one has ever flown before by a pilot whose careful study and preparation was matched by his courage.

Read all of the books in THE AVIATOR'S BOOKSHELF

Prices and availability subject to change without notice

Buy them at your bookstore or use this handy coupon for ordering:

Honoring America's reach for the skies

During 1983, and through 1984, the United States is com-memorating man's development of the science, technology and enterprise of flight since the first ascent in a hot air balloon in 1783.

The Air and Space Bicentennial will reaffirm America's preeminence in aviation and aerospace. But to achieve this, the U.S. Organizing Committee needs public support to mount a national campaign and program of events designed to demonstrate to the rest of the world that America does not intend to surrender its lead in aviation and space technology.

Each supporter of the Bicentennial receives a decal and a copy of the symbol (above) signed by the four-man crew of Columbia during their 1982 mission. You will also receive a newsletter and other attractive items according to the amount of your tax-deductible contribution.

Checks or money orders should be made payable to the U.S. Air and Space Bicentennial and mailed with the coupon to:

Air and Space Boosters
P.O. Box 506, Arnold, MD 21012